MUSIC IN MEDICINE

by

SIDNEY LICHT, M.D.

Fellow, New York Academy of Medicine

NEW ENGLAND CONSERVATORY OF MUSIC
BOSTON, MASSACHUSETTS

MUSIC IN MEDICINE

FOREWORD

In presenting a musician's point of view on so specific a subject as "Music in Medicine", it seems to me necessary at the outset to clarify the status of music as an independent aesthetic art, and its practical adaptation for definite utilitarian purposes. We must clearly separate the active individual process of artistic creation from the elements of passive perception and from effects such perception may have when applied for different realistic reasons.

Taken aesthetically, as an art, music is a social "superstructure", which, as far as the individual creative act is concerned, remains an abstract manifestation of the human mind and imagination. Its existence as a creative art is possible only as long as the practical "possibilities" and potentialities of its effects in the phase of passive perception, do not intrude into and interfere with its character as an absolute non-utilitarian phenomenon in the processes of the creative art. Art, by its very nature is a product of individuality. As opposed to the anonymous craft, the main requirement of an aesthetically artistic product assuming the presence of professional skill and knowledge is that it be the work of a human organism, which possesses acceptable qualifications of vocation and expression. To this attribute we have given such names as talent, genius, imagination, and many others. This phenomenon of specific predestination must also be accompanied by a characteristic property which has received such names as personality, individuality or originality. It is obvious that these fundamentals of artistic creation prevent any general or universal approach to the creative processes which, with the exception of purely technical

ii   FOREWORD

and formal elements of craftsmanship and common expression of specific style, exclude the pattern and definite utilitarian aims. All these factors are obviously concerned only with the living moment of the musical art in the essence and genesis of the individual creation.

Although music as a creative manifestation of the human mind does not aim at social or utilitarian function, its materialized results may yet find wide application in the manifold use of this aspect of passive perception. This passive perception stimulates an active participation by the listener in whom it may provoke definite emotional reactions and mental modulations. If we think of music as the completed creation of one mind, we can understand how its perception may have a genuine influence on the listener's mood and that it may be channeled into desired directions which takes the forms of adaptation and adjustment. This, in spite of the variety of tastes and reactions, can certainly be generalized within limits by scientific methods.

Although I do not believe that music should be written for purely utilitarian reasons (and I am speaking not of the material advantages it may bring the artist, but of the aesthetics of creative art) I see no reason for not using any composition to such practical advantage as its application may offer. Music as an *art appliqué* has been known since ancient times in many different roles, not all as laudable and noble as its use in healing. Its property of melodical expansion, propulsive character, rhythmical vitality, nervous insistance, harmonic intricacy, development in time rather than space, its wealth of moods (which extend from static calmness to wild exuberance with an enormous range of intermediary impressions, even in its abstract character of pure organized sound) provokes in listeners a response which is primarily psychological and emotional, but which frequently influences physiology and the nervous system.

The use of music for work, marches, the stimulation of mass sentiment or emotional impact (patriotism, war, etc.), for entertainment, oblivion, mood change, mood creation, and background music for motion pictures, evokes realistic responses, where music is applied for its effect, rather than for its intrinsic value. It is therefore no surprise that the applied use of music (which has nothing to do with the active process of artistic creation) should be used in the care and treatment of the sick mind and body. I do not know what subjective responses result from such purely physical phenomena as vibration and harmonics but I am convinced that listeners are physiologically and psychically effected by such musical characteristics as mood, intensity, pitch and rhythmical outline. It seems to me that the right music should provoke remembrance and association of thoughts and situations more easily in a mental patient than methods using factual persuasion. Music can avoid the realistic approach and by its absolute progression abstractly recreate a familiarity of situation which may prove most useful in handling mental patients. By eliciting a desired mood it may offer the physician a method of handling disease as important as shock, and a result obtainable in no other way. To a musician, completely unfamiliar with medicine and pathology this use seems obvious and undeniable. Dr. Licht has made a thorough study of this subject and has indicated some of the many uses of music in mental and physical pathology. The work which has been based on scientific research and clinical experience is most impressive and encouraging. If we, as musicians, can bring our contribution to such a wonderful purpose as healing, it would certainly be our most glorious accomplishment for mankind, and the noblest use of our art.

But, as I have said, aesthetically it should not be the aim but the effect of art which should be considered. If *applied use* rather than creation were to assume greater importance, art would lose its essential characteristics and would become a social manifestation of mass production instead of an abstract phenomenon. It might work out usefully, perhaps for a time, but in losing those primordial elements which condition its own existence, it would also lose the *effects* which its use provoke not only in medicine but in other important directions. The effects of music will progress satisfactorily to the advantage of mankind only as long as it is permitted its normal development regardless of motivations and their justifications. In the long run it will find a greater and better use in the practical sense, if its creation continues along traditional lines, and is not diverted into the fallacious channel of anonymous mass production with consequent loss of proper utility and aesthetic *raison d'etre*.

It is likely that scientific research and clinical experience will motivate the production of musical compositions which are designed for certain classes of patients. This will require much skill, craftsmanship, gift of adaptation and assimilation of established patterns as well as disciplined imagination, but the creation of such planned utilitarian works would not be possible without the continuation of music as a self sufficient art activated by its own emotional and spiritual reaction and enjoyment. No derivative may exist and progress by suppression of the source which must aliment it continuously by its own growth and through the conservation of its individual characteristics.

Music as an art has its own internal laws of creation and traditional development. These laws are not casual but organic and they can not be violated without self destruction. Consequently, the beneficial effects of music can be applied for utilitarian purposes only if its integrity is safe from external intervention, even if only temporarily, and if the element of social usefulness does not influence the creative process.

The criteria of artistic and practical values do not necessarily coincide. Artistic value is defined only by time, the practical value is a matter of present usefulness. Works of great artistic value may be useful, whereas facile "hits" which fall into oblivion within a brief period may prove extremely useful, and that is why the two conceptions must be differentiated. Michelangelo's *Medici Tomb,* or a Bach *Mass* are completely useless in the practical sense of the work, and most successful "hit-songs" are completely devoid of any artistic value or originality. Yet both kinds supply the specific wants of those who would lament the absence of either of them. This resolves itself into a question of taste, educational background, musical culture and other factors which I presume are of importance in the clinical use of music. Patients will show preferential response to the music they like regardless of the elements of mood, tempo, rhythm and pitch.

But classifications are always dangerous. Good music is not necessarily useless, and useful music is not necessarily bad music. The eternal principal of *suum cuique* is the principle of individual human taste which can be placed into approximate categories, but cannot be standardized without the artificial interference of external factors. The same principle certainly applies to music as a weapon of healing, where selection should be determined by science but at the same time we must strive to adapt the results of research of the individual preferences of normal subjects.

ALEXANDRE TANSMAN
Los Angeles, January 1946

CONTENTS

Chapter IV

Criteria of therapeutics. Classification of mental diseases. Description of diseases and indications for music.

Chapter V

Counter-irritation. Music in the operating room. Effect on physical exercise. Use with calisthenics. Eurthymics. Remedial exercise. Industrial music.

Chapter VI

Criteria for mealtime music. Examples of orchestras and songs most suitable. List of suggested recordings.

Chapter VII

Needs of children. Slumber music. Bedside radio. Program distribution systems. Head phones versus loud speakers. Personalized music. Instruction in bed. Toneless instruments.

Chapter VIII

Need for entertainment in hospitals. Programming for patient groups. Amateur show. Group singing. Music instruction.

Chapter IX

Basic equipment and personnel. Programming.

Chapter X

Patient band. Instruments and rooms. Record
library. Holiday music.

Chapter XI

Medical direction. Qualifications and duties of
the hospital musician. Training program and curriculum for music aides.

INTRODUCTION

In the middle of the eighteenth century there were two prominent men in Paris whose conflict was typical of the controversial nature of the subject known as Musical Therapy. The Abbé Nollet was not only one of the most prominent clerics in France during his time but was in addition the most famous of its physicists. He had constructed some excellent models of machines which produced static electricity, but he had had no medical training. At about this time throughout western Europe, the subject of static electricity had become very popular. Several physicians claimed that it was of great use in the treatment of many diseases. Particularly did they say that it cured paralysis. The Abbé Nollet wrote a book about static electricity and in it told of the cases he had cured with it. The most prominent physician in Paris was Doctor Louis, who was the chief physician at the Salpetrière Hospital, the largest and best known hospital in France. Dr. Louis tried to repeat the cures promised by Nollet but was unable to secure success in any of the patients whom he exposed to static electricity. He published the story of his failure to do so, which so excited Abbé Nollet that he wrote an entire volume condemning Dr. Louis. Instead of refuting the ability of Dr. Louis to diagnose paralysis and evaluate a cure, he climaxed his remarks with the classical question addressed to the doctor, "Is electricity your field?" (61)

For many centuries philosophers and musicians have claimed the ability to cure mental illness through the use of music, and have at times called this procedure Musical Therapy. Although the physicians might well say to these musicians that therapeutics is definitely not within the province of musicians, it is unlikely that a musician would at this time have the courage to ask physicians, "Is this your field?"

A thorough search of the history of medicine will show that almost all phenomena and substances have at one time or another been tried in an attempt to combat disease. Many of these agents were abandoned when they became unfashionable to a more sophisticated civilization, or were recognized as unwholesome by a more educated generation. The fact that few were given up merely because of their ineffectiveness can be seen in the great number of quack nostrums which still enjoy an active sale among the ignorant, and by the impossible claims of highly organized cults which continue to gain in numbers and followers in this country. Healing schemes based upon the use of herbs because they are delivered right from nature's womb, or the fanciful notion that all diseases arise from the imaginary displacements of the spinal bones, are still in their ascendency. The liberal system we call democracy has not only permitted their growth but has rewarded their ingenuous and ingenious development. Exposure of the fraudulent methods involved serves little purpose because the mentality which is so susceptible to warped reasoning responds poorly or even antagonistically to enlightening guidance.

There are, however, certain valuable features in herb and spinal doctrines which have been partially ignored by reputable physicians because of the intimate relation of these ideas to cult practice.

In spite of a spirited rebirth of the movement towards the establishment of a system of healing based on music, there are many valuable uses of music in medicine which might suffer a like fate unless a critical analysis of the worth of music as a therapeutic agent is effected before Musical Therapy reaches the dubious distinction of classification as a healing cult.

This book has been written with a view to preserving for

medicine that which is good for patients, and in an attempt to aid musicians under medical guidance in using music to help the sick.

Primitive peoples throughout the world still use music in association with the healing arts. This of course is an indication that they have probably used it for more centuries than are recorded in the pages of written history. Ancient civilizations frequently associated music with the divine, but placed diminished emphasis upon its association with healing. Even so, the Hebrews accredited to music curative and inspirational powers (7), as can be seen by the reference in Scripture: "And it came to pass when the evil spirit from God was upon Saul that David took a harp and played with his hand; so Saul was refreshed and was well and the evil spirit departed from him." (63)

For the Greeks to whom we owe the origin of the word music, Apollo served as the God of both medicine and music, and there were some among them who suggested its use for both mental and physical disease. "Plato and Aristotle claimed that the Dorian mode was regarded as virile, energetic, and proper for the perfect citizen; the Phrygian made them headstrong and the Lydian included effeminacy and slack morals. The modes of Asiatic origin were considered suitable for banquets." Five hundred years before the birth of Christ, Pythagoras* founded a brotherhood "based on music as a means of life and moral uplift." (70) The influence of music was so great among the Greeks that it is not surprising that they used it in all walks of life, including medical treatment. The extent to which they and the peoples who followed them,

---

* Pythagoras passed a black-smith shop one day and was struck with the beauty of the two sounds he heard coming from it. He entered the shop, studied the sounds closely and found that the two notes were an octave apart. This observation stimulated him to a detailed study of music which led to his musical philosophy. He believed that all nature and knowledge were contained in harmonic numbers, and that the world had been made in a musical harmonic accord. He invented a sacred quartenary of harmonic numbers to explain the phenomena of life. But Roussier believed that Pythagoras adapted his system from the Chinese. (70)

used music in this manner will be more fully discussed in the first chapter.

Nicholas Murray Butler once stated that "An expert is one who knows more and more about less and less." There is much truth in this facetious definition. In ancient civilization the known facts were so few that it was possible for some scholars to acquire all the knowledge available. The professional thinkers or philosophers had a comparatively complete familiarity with biology, law, music, medicine, government and theology, and could easily write authoritatively about most of them. Some of the important discoveries in the arts and sciences were made by men equally well known in entirely unrelated fields. As late as the Roman Era, Celsus wrote a series of books on different subjects, each of which was so complete that it was considered an authority in its field. To cite one example, the ten volumes on medicine were accepted for the next thousand years as its gospel text. Although specialization was known to ancient society, its foundation was one of individual will rather than basic training in facts. With the passage of time more and more knowledge developed till the single volume could no longer hold all the known facts of a science and what had been titles of chapters became the titles of books. Knowledge may really be said to have progressed when books are written on subjects about which only one sentence could have been written previously, but knowledge progressed very slowly until the fifteenth century. The Renaissance in art and science developed simultaneously in a relatively small area. The Renaissance of both medicine and music, was in Italy during the fifteenth and sixteenth centuries. Here, instrumental music was asserting its importance over vocal music, and accurate descriptions of human anatomy finally replaced the old erroneous conceptions. Both of these changes were necessary for progress in these fields, but progress was slow in each because there is always a reluctance on the part of the people to accept new concepts. Individuals may be intellectually progressive, but the people find security and comfort in established folkways, whether it be of music or medicine. Fortunately, individuals continued to write of new discoveries and in new idioms, and that which was good was accepted by a few in the same generation and by more in succeeding generations. But each successive step was tedious and it was just as difficult to influence the new generation as it had been the old.

With the growth of knowledge came an increase in specialization and men understood less of subjects unrelated to their own. As the rolling mass of education grew, it threw off tangential bodies of information which moved farther apart from each other, and it is only comparatively recently that these diverging lines have begun to approach one another and offer mutual assistance. Music, the art, found the need for acoustics, the science. Industry has come to accept the importance of color and form, and government has been forced to employ mathematics. There was a time when such combinations would have been considered fanciful; now they are indispensable.

Music and medicine have had casual contacts through the ages, but neither has cried out to the other for help. Musicians and physicians are independent people, brooking no outside interference. There are those on both sides who would protest their marriage, not so much from a concern over connubial bliss as over the possible offspring and undesirable relatives. Medicine has never refused to try anything that might alleviate suffering or cure disease, but it has and will continue to ignore unfounded claims or secret remedies. To be acceptable, therapeutic measures must be applicable to all who suffer, and the ingredients must be available to all qualified practitioners of medicine. Physicians insist that therapeutic modalities be given under their guidance and reserve for themselves the right to evaluate their results. Very few physicians object to the use of music for and by their patients, but many object to calling that use musical therapy. If the musician is aflame with the desire to make music for patients there is no need for insisting that it be labelled anything but music, providing of course that it is music Physicians do not discourage acts of kindness or personal attention to their patients. They want them to have clean bedding and fluffed pillows, but insist that such procedures be called nursing care and not therapy, regardless of the amount of joy it brings the patient. There are many uses to which music may be put in medicine and especially in hospitals. When one considers the number and variety of hospitals in this country, it is difficult to imagine a kind of music which can not find a place in at least one of them, but, for reasons which seem more obvious to musicians than physicians, music has been used in the past almost exclusively for patients suffering from mental illness. During the past few decades, hospitals have given increasing attention to music, and in some instances have developed impressive programs.

In 1944 the National Music Council sent questionnaires to more than three hundred hospitals which treated psychiatric disorders, and received replies from two hundred of them. A summary of the survey was published by them under the title of "The Use of Music in Hospitals for Mental and Nervous Diseases," and some of the information contained in this pamphlet will be of interest to those who are considering this aspect of music as a career. Almost all mental hospitals use music in some form. In half of them, patients participate in music vocally or instrumentally. In many hospitals the use of music is increasing and in a few it is extensive. About one-quarter of the hospitals have some budgetary appropriation for music, such appropriations are not great at present.

Most hospitals look for musical workers among the members of their regular staff; but a few have consulted musical organizations. Trained musicians might think that hospitals would turn more uniformly to musical schools for this sort of assistance, but for the most part, few schools of music have openly encouraged the study of this subject, — in spite of the fact that one-half of all the hospitals questioned stated that they could use additional qualified workers.

Of greater interest perhaps to those who would like to become hospital music aides are the opinions expressed by the hospital authorities on the principal qualifications which they believed musical workers in mental hospitals should have. It must be remembered, however, that questionnaires submitted to hospitals are not answered in a uniform manner, and any survey of this type must be interpreted with caution. When questionnaires are sent to hospitals they usually pass first through the hands of the director or superintendent, who reacts as an individual and not according to a set pattern. One will turn the paper over to his secretary for reply; another will pass it on to a physician, nurse or occupational therapist. In many instances the answers will be filled out by the hospital music worker, and sometimes, if the superintendent is sufficiently interested, he may answer it himself. Each person to whom the questionnaire is submitted may transfer the burden of answering to a subordinate, if he is too busy to fill it out himself. The signature which appears at the bottom of the returned questionnaire is usually one of approval rather than of authorship. Surveys should list the titles of respondents. This one did not. Even if it did, the foregoing possibilities would have to be considered. In spite of this, the qualifications listed will be reviewed for the help they may offer the prospective hospital musician.

A majority agreed that a knowledge of music was necessary, and not only were all phases of music specified, but the ability to make intelligent selections of music and to operate commercial sound equipment was recommended by some. Experience in teaching music, particularly the piano, was high on the list of desired accomplishments, and the faculty of directing singing was even higher.

Many hospitals stressed the importance of a "wholesome personality", but this is a term which defies suitable definition. However, the following qualifications were named: emotional stability, patience, refinement, congeniality, quietness, and a sense of humor. There are further recommendations that the worker should possess: imagination, tactfulness, consideration, energy, perseverance, sincerity, co-operation, adaptability and understanding of human ature. In the final chapter of this work a more realistic approach to this subject will be offered.

One final qualification is mentioned which is to be taken most seriously, and that is that the musician who would work with mental patients should have "a definite urge to help the mentally ill." As a supplement to this he should have or be given a working knowledge of hospital procedure and the handling of the psychiatric patient.

From these comments by hospital authorities and the recent trends in institutions throughout the country, it is reasonable to assume that the demand for adequately trained hospital music aides will increase. Some hospitals will want one or more full-time workers, and others will want a part-time worker. This means that some musicians may be able to supplement their earnings by securing partial pay from hospitals in their communities, the remuneration offered varying with the size of the hospital, its endowment and income. It will never be a source of wealth to a musician, but it can be a stop-gap in the hard early years or a continuous position for those who seek the security of regular employment.

Some people fill positions for which their only qualification has been influence; but in the majority of cases the people who have spent the greatest effort in securing superior training will be the recipients of the best positions. The student of hospital music should prepare for his job as seriously as for any other aspect of music. Regardless of his other qualifications, he must of course be a musician, and a degree in music is valuable; in fact almost essential. The ability to play a second instrument even moderately well is useful. The universal appeal and advantages of the piano make a working knowledge of it important. The music aide should be able either to play the piano at sight or he should study one of the rapid systems of piano instruction for he will be called upon not only to accompany group singing but to assist visiting artists or talented patients.

Although a foundation in classical music is part of any good musical training, a musician who refuses to recognize the importance of popular music in American life is not suited to this work. If he has a positive dislike for popular music, he should look to other fields. It is not necessary that he be able to play all the types of modern jazz, but he should be familiar with the common jargon of jazz and should learn the distinctions which exist between these so-called musical forms. His musical tastes need not be catholic, but his attitude towards the tastes of others must be broadminded.

Advances in mechanical reproduction of music are progressing at a very rapid rate, so the technological aspects of music should be cursorily reviewed. A working knowledge of record players, record cutters, needles, tone control and amplification is not difficult to acquire. It may be part of the duties of a music aide to supervise record cuttings and a public address system. In some hospitals the library of musical recordings and literature may be large. A study of musical librarianship will save much time, and the study of classification systems and filing will become an additional part of the work of a music aide.

More often than not a musician approaches a problem with more emotion than analysis, and this becomes of great importance when the problem is a patient. There have always been and will continue to be physicians who with honest conviction or for greater glory will anxiously ally themselves with anything new or sensational, therefore musicians impassioned with the belief that music is necessary to health will have little difficulty in finding collaborators in the ranks of medicine. Musicians must be cautioned to consider the fact that their sincere efforts may result only in discrediting music, as a therapeutic agent. As a result its acceptance as the basis of such merits as it may possess may be undeservedly delayed because of antagonism aroused by extravagant claims made in its behalf.

Much has been written about music as a therapeutic agent, and recently there have been entire schools and organizations devoted to Musical Therapy. In spite of the great temptation to be in on a coming theory few physicians have associated themselves with these efforts, and what is more conclusive, no physicians of national repute have come forward in approval of the term "musical therapy" as applied to the handling of psychiatric patients.

The use of music should not be limited to mental hospitals, however. Those who have played music for mental patients are enthusiastic over the individual responses they have witnessed. The nature of this response is awakened interest or joy. Joy is a healthful symptom for all patients to experience and this joy should be available to patients in all hospitals. Many other phases of music are adaptable for hospital use and this book is written to outline the many approaches possible and delineate the scientific basis for some of them.

Of the better known books on musical therapy some, like the

work by Hector Chomet, are built around the effects observed in individual patients; others, like the writings of Eva Vescelius, are pure phantasy which stem from unbridled emotion. For science was not applied until the appearance of psychologic investigations when common sense began to emerge from a chaos of wishful thinking. One of the first dependable surveys of the subject was in the *Psychology of Music* by C. M. Diserens. Since the appearance of this excellent work the passages stating his views have been often quoted — frequently without acknowledgment. Its chapter on Musical Therapeutics is recommended for its scholarly history and sober evaluations of facts and fancies.

This book has been written for the musicians who wish to learn how they may work with physicians for patients. Technical terminology has been reduced to simple terms wherever possible for a better understanding, but co-operation can be secured only if the musician is willing to forget his preconcieved ideas and abide by the decisions of the physician, who may not be too familiar with music but is familiar with hospitals and patients.

The unemotional approach to this subject is of recent origin. Little has been written in that vein, and this book will lay no claim to originality or perfection. It is hoped that it will act as a guide to further study and an aid to those who wish to engage in this as yet uncharted venture.

Realizing that few sources of information are available in this field to musicians, and that some musicians may one day feel the urge or experience the need to participate in such work, the New England Conservatory of Music invited the author to give a series of lectures to its students on this subject. At the conclusion of the course they decided to offer this outline to those who might later wish to refer to its contents.

In preparing this work the author had the good fortune of personal interviews with some of the leading musicians, musicologists and musical psychologists in the country. Although no statements which appear in this volume are to be construed as the opinions of any of them, an expression of thanks is offered to the following for their willingness to exchange ideas with the author: Dr. Serge Koussevitsky, Mr. Igor Stravinsky, Dr. Harold Spivacke, Dr. James Mursell, and Dr. Carroll Pratt.

The author wishes to express his thanks to Mrs. Margaret E. Gurney and Miss Ida Evans for their assistance in the preparation of the manuscript.

The author wishes to express his deep gratitude to Mr. Clifton Joseph Furness, Director of Academic Subjects at the New England Conservatory of Music for his supervision in the editing of this book.

S. L.

CHAPTER ONE

HISTORY OF MUSIC IN MEDICINE

"Music exalts each joy, allays each grief,
Expels Diseases, softens ev'ry pain,
Subdues the rage of poison and the plague,
And hence the wise of ancient days ador'd
One pow'r of Physic, Melody and Song."

"The Art of Preserving Health"
by John Armstrong (1709-1779)

In many fields of endeavor a scholar occasionally appears who
not only makes a personal contribution to the knowledge and
advancement of his subject but summarizes previously gained information so well that his work becomes at once a milestone and
a beacon. In the field of music, such a man was Charles Burney,
who began to publish a *General History of Music* in 1776. This
book was so thorough and scientifically critical that his conception
is as modern as tomorrow. After listing all the instances of music
as a therapeutic agent, he concludes:

"Yet men delight in the marvellous; and many bigoted
admirers of antiquity, forgetting that most of the extra-
ordinary effects attributed to the music of the ancients
had their origins in poetical inventions, and mythological
allegories, have given way to credulity so far as to believe,
or pretend to believe, these fabulous accounts, in order

to play them off against modern music, which according
to them, must remain in a state far inferior to the ancient,
till it can operate all the effects that have been attributed
to the music of Orpheus, Amphion and such wonder-
working bards." (15)

It is well to begin a study of music in medicine with Burney's
restrained enthusiasm lest we fall into the error of building impossible temples of healing on the thin ice of untested claims. We
shall begin with prehistoric times.

The use of music against disease is as old as music itself. In
fact, early history of music is intimately associated with healing.
The wishful thinking of primitive peoples called upon magic for
assistance, and magic is almost universally associated with words,
chanted words, in rhythmic incantation. Chateaubriand believed
that the chant was the offspring of prayers. Among primitive
peoples, the medicine-man combined the offices of priest, physician
and magician, and although all three functions were closely related,
their functions were dissociated on occasion. For instance, there
were special songs for the invocation of natural phenomena, for
group activities, and for accompaniment of healing rituals. "The
belief in the efficacy of musical magic is one of the most important
facts in the history of civilization." (19)

Although no records exist, it is fair to assume that the truly
primitive peoples of today have not changed markedly from their
ancient customs, and that they resemble to some extent the status
of prehistoric men. The universality of certain folkways among
widely scattered tribes of primitive peoples today lends validity to
this theory.

For such studies we need look no further than our own conti-
nent. Even though certain magical practices have been banned by
law, the American Indians number amongst their tribesmen, those

who remember and to some extent still use music in healing. Several investigators have become interested in this study, but chief among them is Frances Densmore who has analyzed and recorded the songs of many Indian tribes. Among the Teton Sioux she found (21) that the sick appealed to the tribal medicine man who gave the case some thought and claimed to find the cure in dreams. "All treatment of the sick was in accordance with dreams." The patient was then placed in a dark tent and the medicine man sang his dream song, as well as songs addressed to the sacred stones. The use of herbs of the agency of magic might accompany the song. An example of one of the songs used to cure wounds has the following text:

> "Behold all these things
> something elk-like
> you behold
> you will live"

Words like these have a certain sophistication which we may assume constitutes a more recent development.

For many centuries primitive peoples have had different concepts of the exact nature of disease, but for many of them it connotes some connection between a demoniacal spirit and counter-spirits. There were a great many methods employed to drive out the evil spirits. The idea that music was efficacious in these cases persisted for centuries. Martin Luther said, "The devil is a saturnine spirit and music is hateful to him and drives him away from it."

Densmore points out that among the Iriquois (22) the word *orenda* is used to designate the universal indwelling spirit. Nothing was regarded by the Indian as supernatural, in our use of the term, but many Indians desired an *orenda* stronger than their own. When a medicine man began to treat a sick person the result depended upon the power of his *orenda*. *Orenda* could be put forth in song. Those who possessed *orenda* strong enough to do wonderful things were called medicine men. They were consecrated to their work, and the safety, success and health of their people depended on their efforts.

In completing her analysis of Indian medicine songs, Densmore concludes that they suggest "the confidence which the medicine man felt in his own power, and which he wished to impress on the mind of his patients."

Wallaschek (79) lists many examples of the healing use of music among primitive tribes. Among the Wasambara in East Africa, the doctor arrives with a small bell in his hand which he rings from time to time. The patient sits before him on the ground and the doctor begins speaking in a singing tone: "Dabre, dabre." He repeats this several times and the patient sings a simple response. In Australia, Wallaschek found a tribal doctor shaking a bundle of reeds, an action otherwise used during a song to mark time. In Borneo, the natives perform recitatives and songs in order to catch the soul of the patient which is supposed to have run away before the evil spirit. The Wallawalla Indians in this country believe that song influences the cure of a patient, and all the convalescents are directed to sing for several hours daily. In British Columbia the doctor sings when he visits the patient, while a chorus of people intones a song outside the house.

With the dawn of civilization, intellectual activity became more progressive but folkways die hard.

"The ancient Egyptians called music 'physic for the soul,' and had faith in its remedial virtues. We may presume that the incantations presented in the medical papyri were likewise to be emitted with the proper voice and therefore contain an element of

music. The Persians regarded music as an expression of the good principle Ahura-Mazda and are
said to have cured various maladies by the sound
of the lute" (24) "The Lacedemonians agreed with
the Egyptians and confined the possessors of music
to one family, and their priests like those of Egypt
were taught medicine and music, and initiated into
religious mysteries" (28).

The martial and moral values of music were appreciated by most
of the early civilizations. Both Confucius and Plato believed that
music was the most certain means of reforming public mores and
sustaining them at a high level. (25) Although many histories
on effects of music quote the scripture as evidence of the Hebrew
use of music in healing, the passage quoted (63) is subject to
various interpretations. It simply says that after listening to
David play on the harp, Saul was "refreshed and well," this
could refer more to loss of fatigue than cure of a disease.

The great poets have always sung the praises of their beloved
sister muse. In Homer there is a story relating how the flow of
blood from Ulysses's wound was stopped, charmed by the use of
music. (13) Now it is very possible that the blood of the famed
warrior coagulated in its wound during a musical interlude, but
then, all wounds except those involving a large artery will cease
bleeding in about twenty minutes. Homer also stressed good
music and song as a means of elevating the spirit and of over-
coming depression of the soul or mind, agony, anguish, anger
and sorrow. He gives as an example the story in which Chiron
heals the sick with melody. (57) Cato (13) spoke of luxated
joints which were eased by the harmony of sound. We cannot be
sure of the diagnostic acumen of the observer, but for active people
the most common traumatic joint trouble is a "locked" knee. Most

knees which contain disturbed cartilage will unlock after a relatively short period of rest. In each of these instances, music was an
environmental coincidence. Such observations would only begin to
assume scientific medical value if they could be repeated many
times under identical or similar conditions. They were not.

We may now return to the episodes related by Burney in his
commentary. Martianus Capella, an ancient author on music,
assures us that "I have often cured disorders of the mind as well
as the body with music" (58). He also claimed that the Aesclepi-
ades, the state-recognized priests of medicine, cured deafness by
the sound of the trumpet. "Wonderful, indeed!", says Burney,
"that the same noise which would occasion deafness in some should
be a specific for it in another." In Plutarch's book *De Musica* it
is related that Thaletas the Cretan delivered the Lacedemonians
from the pestilence by the sweetness of his lyre.

> "Thaletas, a famous lyric poet, appeared by command
> of an oracle and all the songs he sang were prayers
> to the Gods. The disease probably reached its high-
> est pitch of malignity before he came, and began to
> subside with his coming; but its disappearance was
> attributed to the music of Thaletas."

Many other cures are cited. Xenocrates employed the sound of
instruments in the cure of maniacs; and Appolonius Dyscolos
claimed that music was a sovereign remedy for dejection of the
spirits and a disordered mind, and that the sound of a flute would
cure epilepsy and sciatic gout. Athenaeus rendered the cure for
gout more certain by playing music in the Phrygian mode, while
Aulus Gellius insisted that the music be soft and gentle, the
opposite of the furious Phrygian. Coelius Aurelianus introduced
a concept which reappeared at several widely separated times.
He called it *loca dolentia decantare,* or enchanting the disordered

places. He claimed that the pain was relieved by causing a vibration in the fibres of the affected part. There is little doubt that music causes a physical vibration of the air, but the force that such vibrations could have on most tissues is negligible. Other writers recommended that the instrument be held against the part to be treated for direct transmission of the vibrations, but if physical excitement is desired this can be accomplished more uniformly by applications known as manipulation or massage. Such manipulations are known to be helpful in some conditions, but not curative in painful conditions such as sciatica.

Nearchus, who accompanied Alexander the Great in his conquests, reported that in India the only remedy against the bite of a serpent was a chant (70). Galen, one of the soundest physicians of ancient Rome, recommended music as an antidote to the bite of vipers and scorpions (7), and for centuries music was recommended for the bite of a tarantula. In the seventeenth century three physicians named Mead, Burette and Baglivi explained this use of music. They said that it threw the patient into a violent fit of dancing which brought out a plentiful perspiration, and with it the poison. Since perspiration consists of water and a few simple salts, such activity would increase the concentration of the poison in the circulating blood, and neither the explanation nor the treatment is acceptable (28). Music was recommended not only for the bites of the reptiles and insects; Desault recommended it in the treatment of hydrophobia (23). Not all bites are poisonous, and it is likely that in the case of the two patients mentioned the cure was more for fright than bite.

The effects of music on the mind were too obvious to escape the ancients. When the armies of Greece took the field, they were accompanied by the best musicians, who by their martial strains inspired the soldiers with a kind of mechanical courage never experienced by their enemies.

The distinction between mental health and disease was not advanced among the ancients, but they did recognize varieties of insanity such as delerium, melancholy and mania. Many physicians recommended music in the treatment of mental disease, and Quarin spoke of a single case of epilepsy cured by music. With the exception of severe epilepsy, many patients who suffer from the symptoms which bear this name have only occasional attacks and these disappear spontaneously, making the music simply another coincidence.

Celsus, who was a great medical authority not only in his own time but in subsequent centuries wrote of the mentally ill, "We must quiet their demoniacal laughter . . . and sooth their sadness by harmony, the sound of cymbals and other noisy instruments" (16). Areteus, another great physician of ancient Rome, prescribed music for "corybantism," a disease of the imagination" (24). The great Dutch physician, Boerhaave (11), said, "I do not know if all that one tells us of the charms and enchantments could not be attributed to the effects of music, in which the ancient physicians were well versed." References continued to appear concerning the magical relationship between music and healing. Robert Grosseteste (1175-1253 A.D.) said that disease and even wounds and deafness could be cured by music based upon a knowledge of astrology and mathematics (75).

During the early part of the Christian Era, most of the arts were sustained by the Church, and as a result the finest works in painting and music were available to the average man only within places of worship. Not until the Renaissance did serious music take on a secular character. Music until then was largely identified with religion, and as such was considered to have an influence on the soul. Bacon advanced as a rule of health that people "recreate

their spirits every day with a piece of good music." (13)   He went
a step further in his *Sylva Sylvarum.*

> "Seeing then the mind is so powerful an agent in
> particular disease, I see no reason why the efficacy
> of music should not be tried in many disorders which
> arise in the animal constitution; for music composes
> the irregular motion of the animal spirits and more
> especially allays the inordinate passion of grief and
> sorrow." (7)

The restful and joyful qualities of music were praised by Shakespeare:

> "But sweet music can minister to minds diseased
> Pluck from the memory a rooted sorrow
> Raze out the written troubles of the brain
> And with its sweet oblivious antidote
> Cleanses the full bosom of all perilous stuff
> Which weighs upon the heart."

Henry Beacham wrote in his *"The Compleat Gentleman"* in
1634 that

> "the exercise of music is a great lengthner of life,
> by stirring and reviving the spirits, holding a secret
> sympathy with them; besides the exercise of singing
> opens the breast and pipes; it is an enemy to melan-
> choly and dejection of the mind, which St. Chrysos-
> tome truly called 'Devil's Bath'.   Besides the afore-
> mentioned benefit of singing, it is a most ready help
> for a bad pronunciation, and distinct speaking,
> which I have heard confirmed by many great
> Divines; yea, in myself have known many children
> to have been aided in their stammering in speech
> by it alone."

In the dark ages there was very little added to the knowledge of medicine, but during the Renaissance physicians became more progressive and articulate. Among these was the famous Willis who said that

> "Music not only is a delightful phantasy, but dispels sadness from the grieving heart; and it also allays fevered passions and excessive commotion of the breast." (81)

Characteristic of the use of music as an aid to healing is an anecdote quoted by Burney. Farinelli was one of the great operatic singers of his day and his fame was equally great in all of western Europe and England. One of the countries he visited was Spain. "It has often been related, and generally believed, that Philip V. King of Spain, being seized with a total *dejection* of spirits which made him refuse to be shaved, and rendered him incapable of attending council or transacting affairs of state; the Queen who had in vain tried every common remedy that was likely to contribute to his recovery, determined that an experiment should be made of the effects of music upon the King, who was extremely sensible to its charms. Farinelli was summoned and on his arrival her Majesty contrived that there should be a concert in the room adjoining the King's apartment, in which the singer performed one of his most captivating songs. Philip appeared at first surprised, then moved; and at the end of the second air, made the virtuoso enter the royal apartment. He plied him with compliments and caresses and asked him how he could sufficiently reward such talents, assuring him that he could refuse him nothing. Farinelli, previously instructed, only begged that his majesty would permit his attendants to shave and dress him, and that he would endeavor to appear in council as usual. From this time the King's disease gave way to *medicine,* and the singer had all the honor of the cure. "The King," according to the *London Daily Post* of September 26, 1736, "settled a pension of 3,150 pounds sterling, per annum, on Signor Farinelli, to engage him to stay at court."

A great number of references during the sixteenth and seventeenth centuries attests to the wondrous workings of music against mental disturbances. Wilhelm Albrecht (1) reported a patient who was suffering from melancholia. Many remedies had been tried, when as a last resort the physician requested that a certain *ritournello* be played. As soon as the patient heard it, he began to laugh with all his might and hopped out of his bed completely cured. More interesting is the observation of Champlain (17) who wrote on his return from America, "It is the custom in America when one is sick, to divert them with loud music, to prevent brooding about the condition and thus help restore health."

Mozart was not the first to call the flute "magic." To Democritus was attributed the story of abolishing plague with its music. Jean-Baptiste Porta claimed that one could cure all disease with music, provided that one used a flute made of the wood of the plant which was a known specific for the disease to be treated. Thus one could cure mental disease with flutes made of hellebore stems. One could return some vigor to the impotent with flutes made of orchid stems, and fainting could be cured by playing on a flute made of cinnamon wood. (67).

Phillipe Pinel, the physician credited with being the first to accord the mentally ill humane treatment reported at least one instance of the use of music in the treatment of epilepsy.

> "During the attacks, the sense of hearing, far from being deadened, seemed to have acquired more keenness. A skilful musician played on the violin at the patient's side during her paroxysm. Although she then appeared insensible to the charm of music, she

was so strongly effected by it, that she admitted after
after having recovered entire consciousness, that the
music had thrown her into a state of rapturous
delight."

Literature abounds with many accounts of the use of music
by lesser medical lights. Sauvages (18) mentioned a young man
who had attacks of intermittent fever accompanied by violent
headaches which could be soothed only by the sound of a drum
played loudly. This same patient did not like music when in
good health. Instances of this nature may be explained on the
basis of counter-irritation, wherein a new disturbance super-
imposed upon an old one may counteract it.

In the eighteenth century, Brocklesby (13) summarized the
known literature of music in relation to health and disease and,
considering the status of medicine in his day, made a fair appraisal
of its value.

During the last century Hector Chomet (18), a Parisian physician, became interested in music and its application to disease.
He wrote a short article setting forth his views, which he was to
deliver to a group of medical men in Paris, but was put off time
and again by his colleagues and by political upheavals. Each time,
before replacing his paper on the shelf, Chomet made additions.
This work grew to be the important thing in his life, and when
he could contain himself no longer, he published a book on the
subject which showed considerable research but which unfortunately contained as much invention as fact. Not content with the
known and proved existence of blood and lymph as the chief body
fluids, he added another — the "sonorous fluid," which was influenced for the good or bad by the vibrations of musical sounds.

At about the turn of the century Eva Vescelius, a woman of
great charm, beauty and perseverance, reintroduced the use of

music for mental disease under the guidance of a physician. There is little doubt that she gave great joy to many patients, but a differentiation must be made between personal attention and therapeutics. In her works (78) on the subject one can read enthusiastic accounts of past performances, but unfortunately her explanations and claims are pure phantasy, to wit:

> "For fever, high pulse, hysteria, arrest the attention, play softly and rhythmically to bring pulse and respiration to normal. Tests with instruments will prove that music will do this. Do not change too abruptly from one key to another; modulate and pause and let the musical impression be absorbed. Select songs that depict green fields and pastures new, the cool running brook, the flight of birds, the blue sky, the sea.

> "Fear is dissipated by music awakening in the listener the consciousness of the all enveloping Good. A high nervous tension is relieved and nerves are relaxed under the spell of a composition that swings the body into normal rhythmic movement. Sluggish conditions of body and mind are eliminated by the rhythmic waltz, polka or mazurka — music affecting the motor system. Insomnia is cured by the slumbersong, the nocturne, or the spiritual song that assures one of the Divine protection."

The use of music in hospitals is by no means limited to the application to mental disease. Recreation is needed to avoid boredom, for as Shakespeare said:

"Sweet recreation barr'd, what doth ensue
But moody moping and dull melancholy
Akin to grim and comfortless despair
And at her heels a huge infection troops
Of pale distemperatures and foes to life."

The use of music as a diversion in hospitals received a great impetus in the First World War but made its greatest leap forward with the introduction of the portable bedside radio.

The use of music as an exercise for poorly moving joints and weakened muscles is recent and may be said to have received its great impetus in the Second World War (described in the Boston Sunday Post, February 11, 1945; A-5).

CHAPTER TWO

PHILOSOPHY AND PSYCHOLOGY
OF MUSIC

I

In the realm of thought, opinions and theories sometimes find credence long after they have been proved incorrect. In the field of the arts, opinions may become so strongly rooted that there is occasional resistance to any analytical attempts designed to disprove them, and even after they have been exposed, there will be a significant number of people who will continue to believe in them. The artist who would make music for patients must approach such an endeavor with a full knowledge of the elements involved, and should be willing to recognize those prejudices, customs and thoughts concerning the effects of music on the human body which have been fostered by well-meaning, but misguided, enthusiasts. We must differentiate between the philosophy of esthetics and the proved psychology of music. Musicians who refuse to accept those results of scientific research which disagree with their personal views will fall into the same difficulties which have beset so many musicians in the past who have desired to help patients.

Before the advent of laboratory psychology, there was no satisfactory test for the theories which dealt with music and the mind, and the number and variety of theories advanced were great. Some of the most unreasonable were the most attractive, and it is easy to understand why they were accepted. But if any of these theories is used as a means of attaining a scientific end it cannot succeed with any dependability if it is unsound.

The psychologic effects of sound may be physiologic or intellectual. They may be related to intensity, quality or direction on the one hand, or to past or present mental associations on the other. To the primitive man thunder, which seems to come from everywhere and is louder than anything he can produce, is terrifying and supernatural; the rustling of leaves is frequently caused by the wind, but from his past experience may also instil the fear of the approaching enemy. Sound is often frightening from its qualities or implications.

The psychologic reaction to the type of sound known as music may vary from the reflex panic produced by the air-raid siren to the soothing effect of a softly sung lullaby. For some people, certain musical selections elicit almost no response, while in still others a truly amazing chain of mental images results. The latter reaction is the result of centuries of evolution in the development of music and knowledge, and will be discussed later.

During the modern evolution of musical composition, many new forms were devised bearing descriptive names. Some of these forms by their distinctive tempo, dynamics, or title conditioned the informed listener to a mental attitude consistent with the intention of the composer. Some selections by the very nature of their execution cause stimulation or assist repose. Superficially it might seem, therefore, that the controlled administration of music could evoke desired moods in listeners at will, and some practitioners declared that music is a specific treatment for mental disease. It is undoubtedly possible to influence the mood of healthy, trained musicians by the use of selected compositions but to assume that all listeners will react in similar fashion, or that the moods of the mentally deranged can be changed at will by prescribed music, is to ignore the nature of mental disease and the scientific finding of psychologists.

Music is many things, but physically it consists of sounds or notes which have pitch, intensity, timbre and duration. These notes are combined in patterns which have rhythm, tempo, melody and harmony and these in turn are related to key, mode and form. Each of these elements has been the subject of philosophic interpretation, and more recently of psychologic investigations. Although the effect of music on the human mind depends upon the reaction to the entire composition, it is important to review the existing data in order to understand more fully the effects of music, in spite of the difficulties; for as Ortman (71) has said "the problem of analyzing and classifying responses of music into types is at the same time intensely interesting and notoriously difficult. The history of the problem is rich in unco-ordinated data and poor in clear-cut conclusion."

II

ELEMENTS OF MUSIC

Pitch. Heinlein (45) found that the same chords which called forth a happy and bright feeling when played in high pitch were characterized as gloomy or melancholy when played in low pitch. The voice of youth and laughter is higher pitched than the grumbling of old age and may be a conditioning factor. Beaunis (8) felt that the reaction to pitch is the effect of experience and custom and cited a reversal among Orientals in whom low pitched sounds effect joyous reactions and the high, sadness and sorrow.

Intensity. Heinlein found that loud chords are rarely soothing, and soft chords are almost always soothing. Beaunis stresses the fatiguing quality of great intensity over a long period, and contrasts it with "Very soft sounds as in Schumann's 'Danse des Sylphes' . . . which holds you under the charm of delightful emotion."

Timbre is the quality of sound which identifies it with the instrument of its production. Although many instruments can be convincingly gay or subdued, most authors are agreed that some instruments emit prejudicing tones. Chomet (18) considered the bassoon mournful, the flute tender, and the trombone harrowing. He found that the clarinet expresses grief, the oboe suggests reverie, but that the violin "seems suited to express all sentiments common to humanity." Mursell (60) finds consistent tactile values in tone. Low tones are dull and high tones cutting. He speaks of the French horn as smooth, the piccolo sharp, the oboe as stringent, the cello velvety and the bassoon rough.

Gundlach (38) believes that the timbre of an instrument is significant in mood response. He finds the brasses triumphant and grotesque, never melancholy or tranquil, delicate or sentimental; the woodwinds mournful, awkward, uneasy, never brilliant or glad. The human voice also has timbre, and distinctive values. There is the dramatic quality of Marian Anderson and the syrupy flow of Bing Crosby; the virility of the basso and the sparkle of the coloratura.

Duration. The sounding of a single note will attract attention, but if the note continues for a sufficient period without changing its characteristics it will become monotonous, annoying and finally exasperating. If the sound is interrupted at equal intervals, this reaction will take longer to develop, but if the intervals between them are irregular, interest is sustained, especially if these variations occur periodically; that is, with a certain rhythm. (8).

Rhythm. It is possible to have music without rhythm, but as Rameau (68) pointed out long ago, "Music without rhythm loses all its grace." Since percussion instruments probably preceded all others, rhythm was the first stage in the evolution of music. The proponents of the motor theory of rhythm feel that muscular response to music with pronounced rhythm is a physiological reflex. They point out that it is difficult to walk deliberately out of time to a well accentuated march, and Dunlap (26) has shown that in reclining subjects "With the utmost possible relaxation of the entire body, good rhythmic grouping of an auditory series can be obtained." With the aid of the electromyograph Jacobson (50) has shown that in complete relaxation mental activity results in fleeting but specific muscle contractions invisible to the eye and unknown to the subject.

Rhythm perception is a mental stimulant. Reade (69) observed that African negroes when ordered to row a boat always began to sing as an aid to overcome their natural laziness. Bücher (14) believed that rhythm as exemplified in working songs facilitates the synchronous expenditure of energy by individuals engaged in a common task.

Althought rhythmic song will not necessarily elicit obvious motor responses in all subjects, the wide-spread use of work songs among groups of people engaged at hard work on land or sea throughout the world is indicative of the value of back-ground rhythm for communal effort. Mursell (60) believes that "any notion that pure or 'naked' rhythm is more effective than rhythm clothed in tone is open to very serious doubt." But the chief effect of marked rhythm is the feeling of excitement and happiness which it can arouse. Rhythm gives us a certain pleasure because of its orderliness to which the mind is sensible.

Melody as a musical element contributes chiefly to restfulness. (71) If it is simple and recognizable it will recall other times and rest the mind from the thoughts of present problems. If it is complex and new it will distract the more musical but have a less desirable effect on the uninterested.

Mode. The term *mode* is applied to the arrangement of whole and half-tones in the musical scale construction. Of the many possible modes only two are used in our present system of music, the *major* and the *minor*. There is only one form of the major mode, and it is the one most people recall when they think of the scale. There are three forms of the minor mode, but of these the *harmonic* is the most frequently used. It is formed by lowering the third and sixth notes by a half-tone. (80)

When an author pioneers convincingly in a field which has long needed clarification, it is likely that even his questionable remarks will be accepted with the same degree of authority as his scientific statements. In 1722, Rameau (68) published a treatise on harmony which received wide acceptance because of its excellence and comprehension, but in that work he prejudiced many of the writers who followed into believing that the major triad was more pleasing and beautiful than the minor. This concept was not only adopted but embroidered. Hauptman (44) likened the minor triad to the branches of the weeping willow and hence attributed to it a mournful downward drawing power. To the major triad he assigned the property of an upward driving force. (When this is taken literally, as it was, and applied to the patient, we can see clearly why remarkable attributes were claimed for music.)

Now there is little doubt that if the triad of C minor is struck on a piano after that of C major, most people will describe the sensation elicited by the sound of the minor chord as melancholy. Helmholtz (46) attributed the veiled or sad effect of a minor chord to certain notes foreign to the chord which physical reasoning expects.

"The foreign element thus introduced is not sufficiently
distinct to destroy the harmony, but it is enough to
give a mysterious obscure effect to the musical character and meaning of these chords, an effect for
which the hearer is unable to account, because the
weak combinational tones on which it depends are
concealed by other louder tones, and are audible
only to a practiced ear."

But Gurney (40) refuses to admit to a sense of melancholy
in this slight dissonance, for as he points out

"the same slight degree of dissonance as exists in
the minor triad may be made to supervene on a
major triad, by adding to it a certain extremely faint
amount of discordant elements: it would seem then
that the major triad thus slightly dimmed or confused ought to sound melancholy, but it does not
in the least. Another argument may be found in
the following fact. The minor triads of D and A
are of perpetual occurrence among the harmonies of
C major; and yet they do not seem then to convey the
distinctly pathetic impression, instantly produced
by the appearance of the C minor triad.

Music in a major key may be profoundly mournful;
and it would often be impossible for any description
to touch the musically felt difference between such
music and mournful minor music. The minor mode
has a somewhat more constant range of effect."

Such discussions continued until Valentine (76) decided to
test the mood effect of the modes on a group of listeners. He
found that "major intervals are described as sad or plaintive twice

as often as the minor." Heinlein (45) not only substantiated this but found that intensity was the dominant modifier of feeling. He reviewed more than twenty-five hundred compositions for beginners and among them found only seven per cent written in the minor mode. "It is a difficult matter to obtain a composition in the minor mode written for children that does not have a title which relates to the weird, the mysterious, the sad and the gloomy. Apparently composers in their attempts to differentiate the modes for children fall victim to the method of introducing titles opposite to feeling content. To children, the title of a composition is a very outstanding feature. It may be, after all, that reaction to the modes is largely a question of the extent to which association with descriptive titles of a specific variety first establishes the affective impressions in the mind of the beginner." Thus it can be seen that composers have been nurturing an old philosophy by titles rather than music. Beaunis has shown that although among European composers, the major mode has been used for bright and restful passages and the minor mode has been used for uneasy and stirring selections, a study of the music of other races will uncover an entirely opposite use. Hevner (47), in an elaborate series of controlled studies, concluded that "all of the historically affirmed characteristics of the two modes have been confirmed" but admits that "in producing its effect on the listener, the mode is never the sole factor."

In a later study Hevner (48), continues to maintain that modality is effective in the dimensions of sadness and happiness but quite useless in the dimensions of vigor, excitement and dignity.

The reaction to mode is influenced by what has been heard immediately previously, and by musical training. The reaction to mode is not physiologic but offers one key to music for patients

in that those who identify the minor mode with sadness should
not be given such music when gay music is indicated.

Key. There was a time when particular keys were credited
with emotional powers. Lest such thoughts still persist, the following quotation from Gurney (40) is offered.

> "Particular keys are sometimes credited with definite
> emotional powers. That certain faint differences
> exist between them on certain instruments is un-
> deniable, though it is a difference which only ex-
> ceptional ears detect. The relations between the
> notes of every key being identical, every series of
> relations presenting every sort of describable or in-
> describable character will of course be accepted by
> the ear in any key, or if it is a series which modulates
> through a set of several keys, in any set of similarly
> related keys. But as it must have a highest and a
> lowest note it will be important, especially in writing
> for a particular instrument, to choose such a key
> that these notes shall not be inconvenient or im-
> possible; and also the mechanical difficulties of an
> instrument may make certain keys preferable for
> certain passages. Subject to corrections from con-
> siderations of this sort, the composer probably
> generally chooses the key in which the gem of his
> work first flashes across his mind's eye: and when
> the music has once been seen and known, written in
> a certain key, the very look of it becomes so
> associated with itself, that the idea of changing the
> key may produce a certain shock. But the cases are
> few indeed where, had the music been first presented
> to any one's ears in a key differing by a semitone from

that in which it actually stands, he would have perceived the slightest necessity for alteration; and as a matter of fact when a bit of music is thought over, or hummed or whistled, unless by a person of exceptionally gifted ear it is naturally far oftener than not in some different key to that in which it has been written and heard. Even the difference most commonly alleged, between C major as bright and strong and D flat as soft and veiled, comes to almost nothing when a bright piece is played in D flat or a dreamy one in C.

"That a variety of emotional characters can be definitely attributed to various keys is a notion so glaringly absurd that I would not mention it, were it not that it is commonly held; and that such doctrines are really harmful by making humble and genuine lovers of music believe that there are regions of musical feeling absolutely beyond their powers of conception."

In an unnamed manual the following statements occur:

"C major expresses feeling in a pure, certain and decisive manner. It is furthermore expressive of innocence, of a powerful resolve, of manly earnestness, and deep religious feeling.

"G minor expresses sometimes sadness, sometimes, on the other hand, quiet and sedate joy — a gentle grace with a slight touch of dreamy melancholy — and occasionally it rises to romantic elevation. It effectively portrays the sentimental, etc. Another author, quoted by Schumann, found in G minor discontent, discomfort, worrying anxiety about an unsuccessful plan, ill tempered gnawing at the bit. 'Now compare this idea,' says Schumann, 'with Mozart's Symphony in G minor, that floating Grecian Grace.' He quotes from the same writer that E minor is a girl dressed in white with a rose-colored breastknot.

"These are but abstracts, and a good deal of the humor is lost by selection. For the 'characters' of several of his keys the author gives a list of examples the choice of which, inasmuch as every possible character might be exemplified from compositions in every singly key, cannot have been very difficult. It is something like proving that Monday is a day 'especially full of melancholy,' on the ground that some individual lost a relative on it, or that the characteristic of Thursday is 'confidence and hope,' on the ground that on it an individual came in for a fortune."

"These thoughts are similar to that of the Chinese philosopher who traced the five tones of the old Chinese scale to the five elements, water, fire, wood, metal and earth."

Tempo. "The idea of forcing emotional characteristics on tempo is not less preposterous than those on key. (Gurney quotes further ideas of the same writer.)

"The common time expresses the quiet life of the soul, an inward peace but also strength, energy and courage.

"The three-eight time expresses joy and sincere pleasure; but its best characteristic is simplicity and innocence.

"The three-four time is expressive of longing, sincere hope and love.

"It would be interesting to hear from this writer what happens when any one composes a piece in common time, which expresses the quiet life of the soul and 'inward peace' and in the key of E minor, which represents grief, mournfulness, and restlessness of spirit."

Gundlach (38) found that speed was by far the most important factor in distinguishing among several pieces played to a group. And Hevner (48) found that for excitement the most important element was tempo, which must be swift. "Dreamy sentimental moods follow slow tempo. Sheer happiness demands a faster tempo."

Hanson (42) believes that "everything else being equal, the further the tempo is accelerated above *tempo moderato* (which is about the same speed as the human pulse rate) the greater becomes the emotional tension. He goes on to state that "as long as the subdivisions of the metric units are regular and the accents remain in conformity with the basic pattern, the effect may be exhilarating but not disturbing. Rhythmic tension is heightened by the extent to which the dynamic accent is misplaced in terms of metric accent, and the emotional effect of 'off-balance' accents is greatly heightened by an increase in dynamic power." He is unduly alarmed by the effect "Boogie-Woogie" may have on the younger generation because rhythm irregularity finds its most fertile field in this jazz form characterized by "a repeated figure in the bass (which) continues indefinitely in regular rhythm."

Sonority. Hanson (41) has traced the development of music from the highly consonant music of the Roman Catholic Church at about the time of Palestrina to the dissonant music of certain modern composers. He describes the early hymns as "calm, serene and in a sense impersonal." For him, "the expression of personal feeling in music seems inevitably to be associated with the use of dissonance. Indeed the expression of emotion in music seems to be bound up in the contrast between dissonance and consonance, the former producing a sense of tension and conflict to be either heightened by progression to a sonority of still greater tension or resolved by a succeeding consonance." It may be easy for a musician to believe that the increased use of dissonance creates an increase of emotional tension, but to the musically uncultured listener dissonance may just as often create boredom or annoyance.

Composition. Although musical factors such as pitch, intensity and melody can contribute to mood effect when isolated, the reaction to an entire composition is quite different from reaction to tones of chords. It may depend upon environment or association with the situation in which the selection was first heard or is being heard. It may be altered by the length of the composition or unanticipated contrasts of intensity or the use of unusual patterns, rhythm or tempo. In listening to music, expectation plays an important role. A sudden change or interruption is apt to excite surprise. "The mere meeting of the expectation in all its details affords pleasure of a kind. But great as is the aesthetic pleasure, a far greater degree of enjoyment may at times be attained by a carefully planned surprise, the appropriateness and artistic skill of which is recognized and approved" (10).

Much has been written on the images or stories which musical compositions evoke. Some musicians have tacitly implied that ability to appreciate these stories results in greater pleasure, but Gehring (34) wisely insists that "musical enjoyment does not depend on interpretations, but it may also be reaped by those who abstain from making them." There are some people who can interpret any musical selection, and others who find no story. Between these extremes is a group who can get more pleasure from music if listening is preceded by such preparation. As Damon (20) has pointed out. "A musical selection is thought to be more beautiful and more colorful when the usual program notes are supplied before hearing it."

There are those who see specific color in sound. It was Isaac Newton who first compared the diatonic scale with the seven colors of the spectrum from red to violet beginning with C as red. Katz (71) reported on strong color association of two case studies. For the first, C major was jet black and for the other C major was brilliant white. But this could be expected inasmuch as the scale of notes presents intervals and proportions of the most definite kind whereas those of the color spectrum are confluent and have no mathematic relation. Spectrum analogy was discredited by de Marian in 1737 (70). "No two people agree or hardly ever do, as to the color they associate with the same sound" (30).

But color is only one element in a mental image; what about the others? Is it possible for two people listening to a new, unnamed musical selection for the first time to envisage the same story or picture?

T. Kawarski, and H. Odbert (52) found no direct relationship between color and music which held for more than a few individuals but certain general relationships of photoism to special aspects of music were found to recur constantly. Thus increase in brightness tends to accompany rise in pitch or quickening of tempo. Whereas some one factor like strong visual imagery or cultural influences or suggestions may be dominant in some individuals and a totally different factor in another, none of those factors operate in any pure and simple fashion.

Too often musical interpreters will see too much in a given selection. Some will try to rhapsodize in words the theme as announced by the title of the selection. Some enthusiasts will grasp at straws of suggestion from the original source. Gurney cites an amusing instance in connection with a sonata of Beethoven, of which the three movements are entitled: *Les Adieux, L'Absence,* and *Le Retour.* These titles were so inviting that some gushing comments were published about the portrayal of passages from the life of two lovers. However, on the manuscript, Beethoven wrote: "Farewell on the departure of His Imperial Highness, the Archduke Rudolph, the 4th of May 1809." and "Arrival of his Imperial Highness, the Archduke Rudolph, the 30th of January 1810."

The insistence by some of the specific images evoked by certain selections can be disheartening to those lovers of music who accept such interpretations as fact and are disappointed in their inability to experience the same reaction as others, especially if the others are recognized musicians.

> "It is obvious that the power of music to depict objects, situations or ideas is extremely indefinite. No matter how specific a pictorial or dramatic program the composer may have in mind to present through his music, the listener will never get that program from the music itself. If the hearer is told what the music is supposed to depict he will imagine

the incidents and fit them into the music. Or if he
is given a title it will suggest to him a train of
imagery which he will read into the composition.
And if he is given neither title nor program his
fancy might take him on a mental journey, the direction of which will depend upon his mood, his mental
set, his physical condition, his past experience, and
numerous other subjective factors, for which music
serves as a stimulus, but all of which lies outside
of the music itself." (35)

Thus when Rubinstein read into the "Second Ballade" of
Chopin the story of a wild flower caught by a gust of wind, the
struggles of the flower and its final breaking, he confused the
issue by adding a second interpretation to the music which was
inspired by Mickiewicz's poem, "Switez Lake," the story of which
is totally different. When Gilman played this same song for
his students there were many interpretations which ran the gamut
from "meaningless" to "creeping assassins." (35)

Beethoven's complaints of his interpreters and expounders were
frequent and bitter, but we must turn to the writings of the more
literary musicians, Mendelssohn and Schumann, for coherent ex-
pressions on the subject. Mendelssohn wrote,

"What any music I like expresses for me is not
thoughts too indefinite to clothe in words, but too
definite. If you asked me what I thought on the
occasion in question, I say, the song itself precisely
as it stands."

Schumann's position as regards verbal readings of music may
be gathered from the following passage:

"Critics always wish to know what the composer himself cannot tell them; and critics sometimes hardly understand the tenth part of what they talk about. Good heavens! will the day ever come when people will cease to ask us what we mean by our divine compositions? Pick out the fifths, but leave us in peace." (40)

Some musical selections have been written to accompany a subject. Those who know the story of *The Barber of Seville* may associate the aria "Largo al Factotem" with the despair of an over-worked barber, but the same song might have been written to accompany almost any lively subject and for people who have never heard the story and who do not understand Italian, it is just a bright song, possibly humorous. As Gurney says:

"The verbal titles which aim at summing up the expression of certain compositions, however interesting, are so adventitious that they have often been suggested by instead of suggesting the music; and a hundred auditors, if left to guess the title for themselves, would originate a hundred new ones." (40)

Music can evoke specific emotions only when people have been conditioned to it. The "Horst Wessel" song would not stir Americans to hatred unless they could identify the title with the song and its significance. Even then, the degree of hatred or contempt for the music would be variable.

Edwin Franko Goldman's "On the Farm" can leave little doubt in any one's mind as to its subject matter, but with the exception of such very obvious music, or music to which we have been emotionally conditioned, music cannot paint blue skies or green pastures.

What then are the feelings most frequently excited by music? According to Schoen (72):

> "The data show that rest, sadness, joy, love, longing and reverence appear most frequently as the effects produced. Vocal music has a tendency to arouse well-defined emotional effects far more often than instrumental, the probability being that the specific emotional effect is due in the main to the words."

The conclusions of Schoen on mood changes in a tested group sum up the relationship between mood changes and enjoyment. Thus for practical purposes we want to know not only whether a musical composition produces a mood change in the listener, but also what is of greater significance, whether the induced mood is also enjoyed, and to what degree this enjoyment might depend on such factors as the type of mood induced. The listener's familiarity with the selection, and his judgment of the quality of the selection, are also important.

The results of a large series of observations show as a rule, that music produced a mood change in every listener, or that an existing mood was intensified when it conformed with the mood of the music. The tendency of the same composition to produce the same mood in every listener was very marked. The degree of enjoyment derived from the musical composition was in direct proportion to the intensity of the mood effect produced, provided this effect was not due to the conditions of the performance, such as a poor intonation or faulty interpretation.

> "No greater amount of enjoyment was derived from one type of mood than from another type, unless the mood was due to dislike of the specific type of music or to a poor performance. But when the mood change was from joyful to serious, the en-

joyment seemed to be slightly less than when the change was from serious to joyful, provided the hearer was not hampered by a knowledge of the critical estimate of the music to which he was listening or by faulty interpretation. The evaluation of the quality of the musical composition was in direct proportion to the intensity of enjoyment."

III

OTHER CONDITIONING FACTORS

In addition to the physical elements of music previously discussed there are other factors which enter into the type of response of mind and body to music. Mention has been made above of the value of program notes. People who hear new music for the first time may or may not develop a visual or emotional response, but if prepared by descriptive writing they may "understand" or at least enjoy the music more.

"Program notes, oral comments, and the general setting of the presentation are important because they concentrate and reinforce the mood response. Indeed it has been shown that in a verbal introduction offered before a composition is presented, what is said does not matter much, and that almost any kind of comment will enhance the listener's enjoyment if it serves to cue him into appropriate effective states of mind." (60)

Music aides should take this finding seriously and preface the playing of musical selections with verbal commentary. Even popular dance music may be prefaced by remarks about the solo instrument featured or the personalities involved.

With the exception of the effects of rhythm, all other reactions thus far cited have been largely psychologic. Before leaving the discussion of response, one bit of evidence demonstrating possible physiologic action will be presented. Gundlach (39) studied the songs of six different American Indian tribes. Now the language, customs and music of neighboring European countries frequently have something in common, but the absence of the wheel in transportation made the scattered people of the Western Hemisphere strangers to each other. The speech and songs of the different Indian nations are entirely unrelated, yet the songs representing the same types of ceremonials show considerable agreement. From this Gundlach concludes that "music has some conventions grounded on a firm basis of physiologic structure and behavioral similarity of human beings."

A—Live Music. Most people will turn to the source of sound. Even the most phlegmatic will turn if the sound is sudden and loud enough. It is a protective mechanism because identification of the source may prevent personal injury. There is also a sense of satisfaction in the corroboration of the auditory and visual images. When the sound is musical the desire to see its production is greatly increased. For those who cannot make music themselves, it is like watching a conjurer from behind. For musicians it offers the opportunity of inspection, improvement or criticism. One of the most important psychologic components of music is the physical presence of the music maker. About twenty years ago a manufacturer produced piano-player rolls which reproduced the manipulation of well known artists so well that experts could not differentiate between the sounds produced on the piano by a live pianist and the automatic player. Yet this method of reproduction was a failure financially; it had every quality of the live musician except the physical presence.

We demand far less in quality of music from a live band than from a mechanical reproduction of band music. Groups of people who assemble to dance will pay relatively high prices for in-experienced players with a monotonous repertoire for the sake of having live music. The dancers may complain of the poor musical execution, but will suffer a return engagement in preference to the playing of recorded music.

There are cinema stars whose singing voices are harsh to most ears, yet listeners will applaud them into an encore, not so much for the sake of a beautiful experience, but to prolong the human contact. We react not only to the sound, but to the motions and very presence of music-makers. We listen to people as well as their music. Live music stimulates, sustains and focuses attention. It should be used as often as possible for patients. The "live" musician can get patients to listen to musical forms which would be entirely ignored otherwise. If musicians wish to spread the appreciation of "good" music and music appreciation, one method is to be found in personal appearances at hospitals.

B—*The Human Voice.* Of all the sounds of given pitch and intensity the one which best attracts and maintains interest is the human voice. We habitually turn to the human voice. Sometimes we do it as a matter of courtesy. Again, we may do it for better understanding, or even out of curiosity. The spoken language is understood by far more people than is the so-called language of music. When words are set to music they command greater attention than when they are spoken. They are usually compact and in rhyme. We strain to hear each word to gather the full meaning and humor or cleverness of the lyricist. Yet, we willingly lower our literary standards when words are put to music. The verses of many songs sound vacuous and repetitious without accompaniment. But the words are made interesting by the melody, and melody takes on additional meaning from words. "Vocal music has greater power to arouse a definite emotional response than has instrumental music. Rest results about equally from instrumental and vocal music." (71)

Songs with words are ideally suited for arousing patient interest. Community singing is the most valuable form of music for maximum group response.

LISTENING

Violet Paget (55) sent questionnaires to one hundred and fifty people in different parts of the world to obtain a global sampling of reactions to music. From an analysis of their answers she found

> "two different modes of responding to music, each of which was claimed to be the only one in those in whom it was habitual. One may be called 'listening' to music; the other 'hearing' . . . with lapses into merely overhearing it. Listening implied the most active attention . . . Hearing is a lesser degree of the same mental activity where active attention occurs in moments like islands continuously washed over by a shallow tide of other thoughts."

This is very similar to Gurney's classification of musical perception as "definite" and "indefinite." Vernon (52) lists the varieties of response to indefinite listening as:

     a.   Reflex or physiological; soothing or stimulating

     b.   General euphoria

     c.   Stimulation of thought and wandering of attention

d. Emotional moods of interpretation of the so-
called "meaning" of music

e. Dramatic visual images of day-dreams

f. Awareness that sounds are going on, but no
further response.

g. Lapsing of this awareness into the "margin" of
consciousness.

He found reactions a. and b. among primitives and infants; and
reactions c. f. and g. among the untrained.

Schoen (71) found that response to music is related to the
psychologic levels at which they occur, and to sensation, perception, and imagination. The sensorial response is physiologic and
possessed by all. It is the source upon which all other musical
development depends. It requires a minimum amount of mental
effort, and its effects are within the easy reason of the intellectually
inferior and superior alike. As a sensation, music is either pleasant
or unpleasant. Training and experience may lead to higher types
of response, depending upon individual desire and ability to develop musical taste and education. The next higher response is
perceptual and its distribution level adds excitement or repose.
The highest level of response is imaginal.

"Much of the music we hear we have heard before,
and because of this fact we have associated it with
a host of memories with pleasant or unpleasant
coloring. The hearer may not recall the exact time
or occasion on which he heard the selection before
and yet he may have a group of images which are
definitely referred to his own past."

Meyer (71) summarizes the appeal that music might have

for listeners as 1. Emotional response, 2. Suggested associations, 3. Personification of a subject, 4. Its value as an object.

IV

Musical Taste

The selection of music for patients can be handled in many ways. The easiest and least reliable is to use the music best loved by the musician guiding the program. Such programming will undoubtedly meet with the approval of some of the patients but it is unlikely that it will meet with the approval of all. Non-psychiatric patients should be given the music *they* want.

Much has been written concerning specific music for certain groups of patients. There has been considerable prejudice in favor of "good music"; that is "good" in its relation to intellectual values. But music in itself can be neither good nor bad. Its execution or appropriateness for the occasion or the individual may be open to question, but the answer must come from the patient. We must keep uppermost in our minds the goal of music for bed-ridden or chronically hospitalized patients. They look to music as a morale-booster and a source of enjoyment. Most people have favorite songs, but the degree of desire for them or for any music will fluctuate with the time of day, the kind of day, and many other considerations. The taste of the patient will vary not only with age, training, nationality and home back-ground, but with such intrinsic and unfathomable things as personality and thinking habits.

"Musical taste is a folkway, a convention which behaves exactly as do folkways in other realms of activity. Accompanying this taste is the conventional 'conscience' which dictates what is 'right' and what is 'beautiful.' It is more or less impervious to contradiction and is disturbed at the prospect of change" (59).

The music of any given composer does not change but the audience will change as a result of the appearance of new forms of music and living. The works of the eighteenth century, with few exceptions, were loved by its contemporaries but find a small audience to-day.

The musical taste of an individual changes noticeably from childhood to maturity but the change is gradual, and except for those studying music intensively, during any one year of life the change is hardly appreciable. Even established favorites will become less desirable to the individual.

> "After a certain number of repetitions, varying with both the founded experience of the listener and the complexity of the item, the enjoyment is diminished. One might here propose the hypothesis that the rate of ascent to popularity is directly in proportion to the rate of the decline . . . as illustrated by the sharp rise to popular acclaim of the ephemeral popular hits and their subsequent precipitous decline into oblivion." (59)

Among the many factors which sometimes have a great effect on musical taste, contemporary events are outstanding. During a war, the people welcome songs which sing of their prowess, impending victory, or derision of the enemy. Such songs become popular because of their literary rather than their musical content, but they affect taste indirectly, since the only test of taste lies in the songs to which people will freely listen.

Soldiers pick up foreign songs and marching songs and bring

them home as souvenirs and favorites. It is now well recognized how great and prolonged such an influence can be.

Whatever the musical taste of the patient may be, and regardless of how he came by it, it should be satisfied. As soon as an individual attains the status of being a patient, there is an immediate mental depression which may continue to increase if not checked. The patient may develop anxiety, fear, self pity or boredom. There may be sensory depression from pain, unpleasant sight or disability. In addition to these saddening factors there may be undesirable response to environment, personnel, and the monotony of medical or nursing routines. All efforts should be directed at substituting joyful experiences for saddening introspection. The formula for joy is very personal. Although most people will laugh at some comic situations, the response to music cannot be predicted except upon the basis of individual desire. The person who becomes a patient may not have a fundamental change in musical taste but his appetite may be altered by variations in mood, and this is of prime importance.

> "More people express a wish for music dynamically similar to the existing mood than for music of the opposite effect. The amount of enjoyment is slightly affected by the kind of mood change taking place."
> (71)

It is possible for sad music to be more enjoyable to those who are receptive to it, than gay music. Nevertheless, other things being equal, gay music is apt to give a greater degree of pleasure to those who wish to hear it than sad music gives to its devotees.

The enjoyment of music depends not only upon its pleasantness, but also upon its familiarity. This recognition may be one of identity or of idiom. Most people like popular music because they are familiar with its form or tempo; or because they can hum or name it.

The musical taste of the patient can readily be determined by offering him a check-list with the names of fifty or more selections including the entire gamut of musical forms. A general idea of the popularity of classical selections can be determined from the sales records of recordings and the frequency with which certain pieces are performed by the better symphonic orchestras. The popularity of contemporary offerings can be learned from surveys published in such magazines as *Variety* and *Down Beat* or by listening to radio shows such as "The Hit Parade."

Musical taste is closely allied to performance. If chosen selections are played improperly or without regard to certain elementary considerations, the use of music will lose its value to the patient. A brief consideration must include the effects of arrangement, tempo and volume with which the selections are played, since these have been seen to influence the effects of the selection. Many people when asked to name their favorite music will name a performer or a band rather than a specific piece because they have come to desire the characteristic style of the artists preferred, and style in an orchestra is closely related to these factors. Some listeners prefer loud music, but it must be remembered that even though sound does not become painful until the level of 125 decibels is reached, there are some people for whom the painful level is much lower, and hypersensitivity to sound is an important source of irritation. Others may be disturbed by music which is too fast, which must be taken into consideration.

The role of expectation plays an important part in taste. Most people have been conditioned to expect the classic use of the scale and traditional harmony cannot find joy in the unusual tonal structure of the moderns as exemplified in Schönberg or even Stravinsky. Hospitalization is not the proper period of life for indoctrination in the beauties of innovations.

Musical taste is acquired and always relative, and is based as Diserens (24) has pointed out, on the "habit of hearing." An historical illustration of this is the evolution of the consonances. The Greeks regarded the octave as the only genuine consonance. In the fifth century, the fifth and fourth intervals were admitted to this classification. In the eleventh century, the major third was accepted as such, but the minor third had to wait until the twelfth century. "In music the habit of hearing is the Law, and through it, the exception of yesterday becomes the rule of today."

The best analysis of musical appetite can be found in the statement of St. Thomas Aquinas ,"Bonum est in quod tendit appetitus" — the good is that toward which the appetite tends. We repeat there is no such thing as good music or bad music. Music may be played poorly, but the evaluation of the good in music is personal. "Pleasure, and pleasure alone, is the proper purpose of art," said Walter Sickert. Musicians will do well to remember that since taste results from the gradual blending of emotion, experience, and education, it is better to enjoy whole-heartedly "a waltz of Lehar than to be able to make a thematic analysis of a Beethoven sonata and yet remain unmoved by it." (36)

V

SUMMARY

For non-psychiatric patients, musical programming should be based upon patient requests. For stimulation the important factors are rapid tempo, accentuated rhythm, and elevated volume. For sedation, slow tempo and reduced volume are indicated, as well as simple recognizable melodies. Some discussion of the selection to follow is a valuable aid to the enjoyment of listening. Live musicians should be used as often as possible.

CHAPTER THREE

MUSIC AS OCCUPATIONAL THERAPY

Until the latter part of the eighteenth century the institutional treatment of mentally diseased people consisted of custodial care. This meant shelter, food and restraint. The quality of the shelter varied in most instances from very bad to poor. The quality of the food was not as varied—it was just bad. The quality of the restraint was excellent. With few exceptions commitment meant life internment. Violent patients were chained to the wall, for who could tell when they might become violent again after a period of calm? The mentally deranged were not considered as patients with a disease of the mind but as inmates who had lost communal value and social desirability. Dr. Phillipe Pinel of the Salpetriere Hospital in Paris thought otherwise and began to consider these people as still human. Among the reforms he introduced was the use of activities to keep the mind and body occupied doing things. This concept grew slowly at first but eventually reached universal acceptance, was considered of real therapeutic value and named occupational therapy.

During the first World War many military patients were confined to hospitals for prolonged periods while awaiting complete recovery. It was noted that those who busied themselves with such physical activities as required the use of their wounded extremities regained the use of these extremities sooner those who remained idle physically. Thus was born a branch of Occupational

Therapy which was known as *functional* to differentiate it from previous psychiatric use.

Functional Occupational Therapy is used to increase three functions: muscle power, joint mobility and co-ordination of movements. It finds its greatest use in those patients who fall under the care of those medical specialists known as orthopedic surgeons and neuro-surgeons. Orthopedic patients are those who have disease or disability of one or more joints or bones. The most common disease of joints is called arthritis, of which there are several kinds of varieties. The most common disability of bone during war-time is fracture. Arthritis usually prevents complete joint motion. In some instances the joint is put at rest to hasten healing. Almost all fractured bones are kept fixed by plaster casts or traction and prevented from movement during healing. The prolonged rest, necessitated by diseases of bones and joints, permits muscles to become weakened or atrophied, and also permits joints to lose some of their range of motion. When the course of disease has reached that point where rest is no longer required, the chief aim of medical treatment is to restore former function. This means the restoration of power and mobility. This is accomplished by means of physical and occupational therapy. Physical therapy includes the use of heat, massage and guided exercise. Occupational therapy is exercise through work — purposeful, productive work with an incentive. The incentive is twofold — to produce something useful and to hasten recovery.

Patients who have had destruction or other disease of the nerves which activate their muscles develop varying degrees of loss of muscle-power known as palsy or paralysis. When a nerve is pressed or cut, it usually heals in such fashion as to permit return of muscle-power. During the period of its impairment, there is not only a loss of power, but frequently concomitant disturbance in the skin, the joints and still other functions. As a result of the nerve disturbance or the disuse which follows, the portion of the body which is paralyzed loses the ability to use its muscles with facility and maximum economy. There are almost no motions performed by single muscles. Most activity results from the contraction of a group of muscles and these are usually in delicate balance with other groups of muscles which either assist or prevent overaction. The delicate adjustment of muscle groups, which is normally present, results in co-ordinated movements. Following nerve disease or, for that matter, the immobilization of joints and muscles, co-ordination is usually lost to more or less degree. Muscles must be re-trained to work together. Such co-ordination can be accomplished by special exercises, but even more rapidly and efficiently by imitating the motions of life. This is the aim of functional occupational therapy.

There are other disease conditions which can profit from the use of occupational therapy. These include other disabilities which are accompanied by loss of power, motion or co-ordination. When the skin is burned, healing is usually accompanied by some degree of scarring. If the scar includes a joint on its flexor surface (i.e. inside the bend) there will result a deformity known as a flexion contracture. If nothing is done about this, the crippling process will become progressive and some day reach a stage beyond correction other than that offered by plastic surgery. The early stretching of such joints will not only prevent progressive disability but may result in some improvement.

Many other indications for the use of occupational exercise will be met, but since this is not a text on medicine, the preceding types of disabilities will serve as examples of the conditions commonly seen.

The crafts first used in functional work were carry-overs of those most beneficial in mental disease, and for the most part were restful and simple, such as basketry, weaving and the graphic arts. More recently, almost all the arts and crafts have been used, as well as motorized tools.

The results of occupational exercise will depend upon the attractiveness of the objects which can be produced, the energy required, the skill and patience of the occupational therapy worker and patient, and the stage and extent of the disability. For those who are not "handy", or who have become increasingly clumsy with disability, there may be impatience, tedium and fatigue. Occupational therapy is always seeking new activities or modalities as they have become known in practice. Music can be used as exercise in occupational therapy as well as for background and interludes of relaxation.

The fingers of professional pianists and violinists are very strong, for instrumental manipulation requires and develops strength and co-ordination. Music as an exercise can be used not only for its effect on most of the joints and muscles of the body, but to increase the use of the lungs and larynx. It focuses attention through the use of visual, auditory and tactile senses and stimulates mental activity and interest.

Many instruments may be employed for the mobilization of joints and muscles. When a musical instrument is prescribed as the occupational therapy activity for a patient, there may be some resistance on the part of the patient because of a lack of general or musical education, or the fear of studying something new. The success with which this resistance may be overcome will depend upon the skill of the musical aide not only as a musician but as a teacher. The musical aide will have to convince the patient that the fundamentals of music are far less difficult to learn than is popularly supposed. Much of the notoriety about music lessons is developed among children who dislike regimentation, interference with their play periods, and the length of time it takes the minute hand to circle the clock. The musical aide may cite that observation and impress the patient with the greater ease of adults in learning to play. Interest may be aroused by naming the other patients who have recently learned to play and by demonstrating the advantages in earlier recovery that music offers.

Regardless of their initial attitude towards music lessons, most patients will soon be pleased with their progress and ability to master musical notation. Visits to the craft shop will usually be made on an appointment basis and the patient will leave as soon as his "time" is up. The knowledge newly acquired through instrumental instruction will keep the patient at work longer and the musical aide will find him returning for further practice without coaxing and for desirably longer periods.

Piano. Before considering the use of the piano in occupational therapy, the work of Ortmann (64) should be reviewed.

A joint is the point at which two bones connect. In any moveable joint the essential feature is a sliding of one surface on another. Joined to the sides of the two bones near their ends are ligaments which are strong and inelastic and hold the joints within the joint cavity, and which prevent the joint from exceeding its normal range of motion. But the function of holding the bones together and keeping them in different positions belongs to the controlling muscles. Bones are usually activated by at least two sets of muscles which effect the movements in opposite directions. Normally muscles are under a slight but constant tension known as *tonus,* and the simultaneous pull of muscles on both sides of the joint presses the bone surfaces closer, and keeps the muscle in a state which makes immediate action possible.

Joints move by virtue of the contractions of the muscles. Most movements are made not by one muscle alone, but rather by the co-ordinated contraction of various muscles and the simultaneous relaxation of their antagonists. As a result of muscle contractions, a chemical change takes place which produces substances in the muscle that interfere with good muscle action. Ordinarily these waste products are carried away by the circulating blood with sufficient speed to prevent noticeable effects. If, however, the muscle produces these deleterious chemicals faster than the blood stream can carry them away, fatigue results. The earliest manifestation of fatigue is inability to relax, and the second contraction may be initiated before relaxation is complete. The second effect of fatigue is interference with rate and quality of contraction. Only relatively brief periods of relaxation are necessary for complete recovery, but these periods are important. When normal muscles practice on the piano, the fatigue limit is rarely reached, but for the weakened muscles of patients, fatigue must be guarded against by limiting duration of continuous playing and by proper interludes of rest. Ordinary piano-playing offers short rest periods because there is a reflex relaxation after the sound is produced and it requires less muscle energy to keep the key depressed than to depress it.

Muscles are excited into contraction by minute bio-electrical impulses which enter through their motor nerves, but the property of contraction is independent of the nerve and can also be accomplished by artificial external stimuli of electricity or mechanical force. The quality of contraction is a function governed by the health and nutrition of the muscle. The nutrition of the muscle depends upon its blood supply, which depends in part upon its warmth. Delicate motions are difficult for cold muscles and artificial warming is advisable before exercise, a fact which assumes greater importance in cold weather.

From the viewpoint of patient interest and instruction, the piano is the best instrument. When equipped with pianola fixtures, it is the one instrument that gives the widest range of activities. Because the piano is difficult to move, playing is restricted to the room in which it is housed and there need be no concern about its interference with other patients if the practice room is sound-proofed, or is situated some distance from the other patients. The piano offers excellent opportunity for flexion of the fingers and thumb, extension, abduction and adduction of the wrist, as well as flexion and abduction of the shoulders and exercise of the neck and back.

The piano can be adapted for use by patients with extremities in hanging casts, which can be supported by sling arrangements attached to the piano or the patient's neck. It can even be used satisfactorily with a cumbersome airplane splint if a very low bench is substituted for the usual piano chair. The height of the bench can be arranged so that the key-board and hand are on the same level, and the challenge of this position will make the patient try all the harder to use his fingers.

For the contractures resulting from burns of the hands, the piano offers an excellent medium with which to increase joint motion. In depressing the keys the fingers are forcibly flexed. The key surface is much broader and easier to manage than that of the typewriter key. The piano, therefore, offers less of a psycho-logical deterrent to use than does the typewriter. Mistakes at the piano are less annoying because there is nothing to erase but a memory, and the memory of unpleasant things is fortunately short-lived. By means of special musical arrangements and additional notation written next to the printed notes, some fingers can be exercised singly or in any combination desired. The physical exercise or co-ordination of selected fingers can be obtained more subtly by the use of marked music than is possible with most crafts. Some instructors may prefer to mark the keys of the piano with the letters to which they correspond, but this is not really needed in the instruction of adults. A large diagram of the piano keys placed above the musical scale for which they stand may be located to advantage on the wall over the piano.

It is recommended that the first piano lessons cover fifteen minutes and that the time be increased five minutes daily until the lesson fills a half hour period. Inasmuch as the strain of piano playing is very slight, the first lesson may last thirty minutes if the physician so decides. The patient should be encouraged to practice freely at other times during the day as long as his interest can be sustained. Chief attention must be placed on the use of the fingers requiring exercise. As is true in all forms of functional occupational therapy, the impatient patient will try to speed his work by using unaffected joints or by improper use of muscles. The musical aide must guard against this temptation. Although standard music for beginners should be used, it is well for the teacher to use simple arrangements of popular tunes at each session for the incentive that it will give the patient. If the patient expresses the desire to play a certain melody, the instructor should write his own arrangement if none is available.

The keys of the piano can be reached effectively in many ways and it is possible to exercise almost any of the muscles of the upper extremity by playing from different levels. To exercise the muscles of the shoulder girdle, loud notes may be played by holding the hands fixed and raising and lowering the shoulders. The shoulder itself can be abducted and adducted by wide lateral movements along the keyboard. Flexion and extension of the wrist is accomplished by staccato movements. Lateral motion of the wrists is partially restricted by the bony structure but can be accomplished by arpeggio work.

Thumb action plays a very important part in piano playing. The *opponens* action (touching the last finger with the thumb) is very necessary in playing *arpeggios,* particularly with large intervals played *legato.* In fact there is hardly any known purposeful activity which is more useful for full exercise of the *opponens* range than this activity. The music must be fingered with numbers that will keep the index finger on one note as the thumb passes under for the next higher note at an interval of two or three tones. In order to depress the key, flexion of the thumb is necessary. The thumb can be abducted to almost any degree by the playing of chords or by playing *legato* passages.

All motions of the fingers are possible. For active or passive extension of the fingers much use should be made of the black keys. If the hand is held in position to play the white notes in the normal manner, the black keys can be played only by extension. Various degrees of flexion of the joints are possible by ordinary playing. Spread of the fingers which is a function of the dorsal interossei muscles can be accomplished by practising chords, the span of which should be increased as power and range improve.

Violin. In most activities requiring the use of both hands, the more delicate motions are performed by the right hand in right-handed persons. For the violin family the situation is reversed, and these stringed instruments are of greatest value for exercise of the left fingers and right elbow. If the interest of the patient is great, there is no reason why the normal positions cannot be interchanged so that fingering is accomplished by the right hand on a violin with reversed strings.

The violin is recommended for flexion of the left fingers, but is of greater value for flexion and extension of the right elbow. It is secondarily valuable for the flexion and extension of the wrist and abduction and adduction of the shoulder. The motion analysis for the cello and bass viol are similar to that of the violin. The heavier instruments require more motion at the shoulder. String instruments are less popular than the piano because two fundamental techniques must be learned simultaneously; correct fingering and correct bowing. The vibration of the struck piano strings is relatively uniform with variable pressures*, but the quality of the violin sound as produced by the beginner can be discouragingly unpleasant.

Plectrum Instruments. The plectrum instruments afford excellent exercise of the wrist of the right hand and the fingers of the left. The ukulele, when brushed by the fingers, offers better extension of them than is found in most crafts. The guitar offers even stronger flexion for the fingers which depress the strings than does the violin. All these instruments require supination and pronation at the wrist and some flexion and extension of the elbow. They are more popular than bowed instruments and have the added advantage of being so easy to learn that the performer will be able to play simple song accompaniments in a relatively short period of time. The variety of instruments in this category permits a wide range of energy requirements.

Foot Instruments. Although there are several instruments in which the lower extremities are used, there are only two which are readily adpatable to hospital use — the pianola and the parlor organ. For the former, no knowledge or musical ability is required and its use is open to all. The distance between the bench and the pedals will determine to some extent the energy expended and the range of joint motion which can be accomplished. The speed of playing is related to the energy which is required. If

---

* *"a discussion took place in 1913 on the physical significance of that mystic quality called "touch" by which a player attempts to vary the quality of the notes . . . but it was concluded that the velocity of striking was all that could be varied by the player."*

Richardson, E. G. — Sound, p. 106

the library of pianola rolls is large and inclusive enough to meet the demands of the patient's taste, an adequate amount of work can be expected.

The foot-pumped organ is also an excellent ankle exerciser. Even the untrained will find some interest in the timbre of the notes and the qualities of sound emitted with the pulling of different stops. The lingering sounds and the novelty of playing an organ which is no longer a commonplace in the home, are great incentives to playing. Instruction on the organ, which has a smaller keyboard and slower manipulation than the piano, is pleasant and simple. For combined upper and lower extremity disabilities, the organ is an excellent instrument. Every hospital music department should own one. There are enough unused organs in the attics of this country to supply the needs of most hospitals.

The bass drum with foot pedal attached is obviously not a solo instrument, but when used in ensemble or with a full set of traps and snare drum, it can sustain some interest and result in some benefit to those suffering with ankle disabilities. Its use is limited to activity of the muscles and joints below the knee. It can be used by patients wearing a leg-brace pivoted at the ankle.

"Pocket" Instruments. Of all the wind instruments available for the instruction of beginners, those which require no reed or lip knowledge are most desirable. Easiest to play is the "kazoo", or any other instrument which embodies the principle of a membrane vibrating to the sound of the human voice. Only the ability to hum is needed and it is valuable for the patient who is difficult to teach because it permits even the dullest to participate. The kazoo is especially useful for children or psychiatric patients and can supply the melody for "rhythm bands." The ocarina, song-flute and related instruments are relatively easy to master but the

sound emitted is annoying to many. The recorder is easy to play and produces a pleasant sound. The harmonica has been developed into an instrument that is not unpleasant to listen to, but the beginner's efforts may not be too welcome. The fife requires greater effort to operate and is harsh to the ears of some. The flute is too difficult for hospital use and the beginner in his anxiety might experience a "black-out" from sustained blowing.

The reed and brass wind instruments are not suitable for functional use. Their use is limited to chronic patients because of the large amount of time required to learn to operate them satisfactorily.

Wind instruments can be used for patients whose pulmonary pathology has cleared to such an extent that the physician feels lung exercise is indicated. The early use of lung exercise following atypical virus pneumonia has been found especially beneficial.

Wind instruments may also be used for exercising the facial muscles during the recovery phase of facial palsy. Their possibilities in stretching the scars about the mouth and cheeks should be considered.

Percussion Instruments. The snare drum offers motion to the wrists, elbows and shoulders. Few men or children can resist the temptation to play the snare drum. The desire for prolonged playing is not too great, but if recorded music is played during the exercise the duration can be prolonged for an adequate period. The bass drum, as previously mentioned, permits flexion and extension of the ankle when used with the pedal, and this, too, can be made interesting if recorded music is played simultaneously.

Other percussion instruments may not be generally available in hospitals but the possibilities offered by them will be listed. The kettle drum offers rotation of the arms. The xylophone and marimba do not evoke great ranges of motion but bring the muscles of the upper extremities, neck, and back into play, and promote co-ordination. For children, the toy xylophone is a welcome plaything and an excellent form of occupational therapy for the upper extremities. A new toy, the *Typatune,* operated like a typewriter affords opportunity for finger exercise.

There are still other instruments which may be classed as musical that offer opportunities for exercise. It is just possible that a portable hand organ may be available. The novelty of operating one of these is not to be underestimated as an incentive to work, particularly in younger people. Both the hurdy-gurdy and the hand-cranked victrola offer exercise to the wrist, elbow and shoulder. By placing these instruments at different distances from the floor or patient, many ranges of motion can be obtained.

The harp offers excellent exercise to the serratus muscles as well as to the muscles and joints of the upper extremities, but its operation is more complicated than that of most instruments, and even if available, would require the instruction of a harpist, of whom there are too few.

TECHNIQUE

Assignment of patients to instrument-playing should be made in the same manner as other assignments in functional occupational therapy. The physician should prescribe the instrument which best meets the convalescent's needs. He should explain to the musical aide in the presence of an occupational therapist the motions desired and the precautions to be followed. He should set the time limits for the first and succeeding lessons. In general, it may be said that the first lesson should last about fifteen minutes, or until such time as the patient shows signs of fatigue. This period should be extended gradually to a half hour. The patient should be encouraged to return to the instrument as often as is practicable for further study. When the number of patients receiving lessons is large, a regular schedule for additional practice periods will have to be posted. After a relatively short period, the musical phase of occupational therapy will operate smoothly and the physician will be able to delegate most of the details to the occupational therapist, who should frequently supervise the lessons to ensure desired joint motion and to note progress. The occupational therapist should make progress measurements and notes. When properly supervised, the use of music as functional occupational therapy can be as scientific as any other branch of occupational therapy and is the one use of music at this time which may properly be termed "musical therapy".

The following table is offered as a reference for some of the motions possible with a few of the instruments described.

Part	Motion	Instrument
Fingers	All	Piano
Fingers	Extension	Ukelele
Thumb	All but adduction	Piano
Wrists	Flexion — Extension	Piano
Elbow	Pronation — Supination	Guitar
Elbow	Flexion — Extension	Violin
Shoulder	Abduction — adduction	Piano
Neck	All Motions	Xylophone
Back	All Motions	Bass Viol
Hips	Abduction — Adduction	Organ
Knees	Flexion — Extension	Pianola
Ankles	Flexion — Extension	Parlor Organ

VOICE

Singing has long been used for the treatment of stammering and other speech impediments. Singing can also be used to exercise the jaws, larynx, lungs and diaphragm. With proper instruction, singing can be an excellent exercise for the muscles of the chest and abdomen as well as a breathing exercise.

For the patient with a recently wired fractured jaw, singing gives gentle joint motion and restores confidence in the ability to use the jaw again. The same thing applies to patients with recovering tempero-mandibular joint pathology. A patient with poor jaw motion cannot articulate well, but can sing more nearly like the well patient than he can talk. Singing can begin at the level of humming and progress through scale practice to actual song instruction.

When several patients are available for vocal exercises, a trio, quartet or other group arrangement will create greater interest. Except in hospitals devoted to the treatment of chronic disease, the turn-over in patients will make group singing uncertain.

CHAPTER FOUR

PSYCHIATRY AND MUSIC

> "His music mads me, let it sound no more,
> For though it helps madmen to their wits,
> To me it seems it will make wise men mad."
>
> *Richard III,* Shakespeare.

Gaston (31) believes that

> "The basic reason for the arts throughout the history
> of mankind has been the resultant mental hygiene
> benefits. The common creative urge, desire for di-
> version, and search for satisfactory expression exist
> in all people. Music — above all arts — guarantees
> the fulfillment of these elemental urges, and therein
> lies its greatest value."

The suggestive power of music has given rise to a series of legends which go back to the very origin of civilization. But the methods of experimental physiology, so precise in the study of organic function, lead to no clear and easy picture in the presence of reactions as complex and subjective as those of esthetic emotion and artistic pleasures. The task of evaluating the effect of music on the mind is made increasingly difficult by the personal equation, and when to this is added the distortion of mental disease, great caution must be used in the approach, technique, and recommendations to be followed in the use of music as applied to psychiatry

(27). Altschuler (3) finds that music stimulates the libido, which he defines as

> "the great amorphous power, the vital spark, out of which the will to pleasure, the longing for love or passion for procreation take their origin."

He believes that music is the only "medicine" which helps to convert instinctual forces into socially acceptable forms.

> "Stimulated by music, man can still offer his lowly instincts free expressions, camouflaged by jitter-bugging and boogie-woogieing . . . Indeed there is therapeutic acumen to an agent which is capable of reconciling the instinctual with the social, and the sensual with the spiritual."

The relationship between music and the mind is obvious, but the nature of the relationship which has lead some musicians to facile claims of artistry remains for most psychiatrists a tempting but obscure field. Most of the writing on this subject has been done by musicians and so-called results obtained with music in mental patients have been evaluated without medical guidance or the use of scientific method. Physicians are hesitant to accept new ideas which are not founded on unquestionable evidence. Enthusiastic laymen might call this reactionary, and they would not be entirely wrong. It is the reaction to the too rapid spread of folklore, cults, and nostrums which physicians have had to combat to keep medicine on the highest possible plane. It is the only tool with which they can protect the sick from unscrupulous or even well-meaning people who, for personal gain or with ill-founded conviction, promise cures by the citation of accidental or falsified results. By custom, ethics, and state laws the treatment of disease is the province of the licensed physician.

The term "musical therapy" has been applied almost exclusively to the treatment of mental disease with music. The term "therapy" is derived from a Greek verb which means *to cure*. A cure can be practiced and determined only by a qualified physician, or under his direction. Claims can be made by anyone. To establish the curative value of any procedure, certain criteria must be observed. In the first place, the disease must be accurately classified so that the affliction of a series of patients can be scientifically grouped for study. Next, the therapeutic agent must possess qualities of constancy which permit controlled dosage. Last, the proper administration of the agent in the same disease condition must show a reasonably high percentage of results which can be proved to be of value in the control or elimination of symptoms or disease.

Until a relatively short time ago, the causes of most disease conditions were unknown and illnesses were named according to their superficial characteristics. Most newly named diseases are designated by the agents which cause them or by the variations from normal found in the tissues of the body they affect (pathology). In psychiatry, most diseases bear the names applied to their outward appearances.

A simplification of terms places mental disease into three general classes. Psychoses, Psychoneuroses, and Behavior Disorders. The subdivisions of these classes are not universally accepted and the musician who works in a mental hospital will soon become acquainted with the locally practiced terminology.

As a guide to vocabulary rather than an introduction to psychiatry, a brief review of some of the prominent symptoms of mental disease will be enumerated. The scientific material is based on Noyes' (62) excellent text.

The following list of the more common mental diseases is based upon the classification offered by the National Committee for Mental Hygiene.

Psychoses
    General Paresis
    Alcoholic
    Hardening of the Brain Arteries
    Senility
    Involutional Melancholia
    Manic-Depressive
    Schizophrenia

Psychoneuroses
    Hysteria — anxiety, conversion
    Hypochondriasis

Mental Deficiency

Behavior Disorders
    Maladjustment
    Habit or conduct disturbance

Psychopathic Personality
    Amoral, immoral, emotional

Detailed descriptions are contusing to the layman because within one disease subclass, the variations possible as a result of duration, time of onset, mental background, etc. are very great. Only generalizations will be mentioned.

The two major divisions of mental disease — psychosis and psychoneurosis — are not always readily differentiated. In the psychotic, the personality is usually distorted, whereas in the psychoneurotic the personality remains normal in relation to the realities of the world and social life. The psychotic is the more obviously deranged, the psychoneurotic usually passes for almost normal.

General Paresis is a late result of syphilis. The patient becomes increasingly forgetful and disinterested in his surroundings and social relations. There is a gradual loss of judgment and other mental faculties. The facial expression becomes empty and the speech slurred. This is the disease in which the knee reflex disappears, an indication popularly associated with "crazy people". It is a progressive disease which becomes more difficult to treat as it progresses. The treatment at this writing consists of the use of drugs containing arsenic and the production of fever in the patient. The results are not remarkable, ordinarily. Return to normal is unusual. Music for such patients could in no manner be conceived as curative or even helpful.

Alcoholic Psychosis results from continued excesses of drinking. The patient usually resents criticism because he is convinced that his reverses have driven him to drink. The prolonged use of alcohol relaxes inhibitions, produces anti-social actions, and results in more sorrows to drown in more alcohol. Alcoholic psychosis usually begins suddenly with mental confusion, muscle twitches known as tremors, and vivid, visual imaginary thought known as hallucinations. The treatment for such patients includes withdrawal of alcohol and the use of sedative measures. One of these measures is a prolonged bath in a tub of water just below body temperature. Once the patient has recuperated to the convalescent stage, music may be employed. Some alcoholics like to join in group singing, especially if the group is made up exclusively of fellow inebriates. Any encouragement to join non-alcoholics in group singing, or any use of music which may stimulate a permanent interest in a new instrument or diversion would be valuable. These patients lack self-imposed discipline. If music can be used as a discipline, it might lead to decreased drinking.

Arteriosclerotic Psychosis. As its name implies this is a condition of the aged and is probably related to hardening of the brain arteries. The symptoms may include emotional instability, mental fatigue, disinterestedness, and some loss of memory. The patient begins to look and act old. The treatment consists of custodial care, physical rest, and mental occupation. Music is well suited to this combination. Oldtime favorites played softly for several periods daily is indicated. Obviously, where specific musical numbers are requested they should be played.

There is another disease which resembles this called senile psychosis. Usually it can be handled in the home, and is.

Involutional Melancholia occurs at an age when certain important biologic functions of the body begin to regress or involute. For women this age is usually forty-five, but for men it can be ten or more years later. The condition is seen especially in those who did not lead an average life previously. A study of the personality of such patients usually shows them to have been uninterested and uninteresting people, with few close friends. An unfavorable experience may bring on worry and unrest. They become saddened and exaggerate the minor sins of their past. They develop false beliefs known as delusions about their surroundings or themselves. At least half of them never recover completely.

There is little that can be done for them, except to encourage healthful diets and hygienic regimes to keep them physically well. Some physicians might encourage the use of music for such patients to distract their attention from themselves. Familiar melodies are recommended, because of the age group, old time favorites will be the most suitable.

Manic-Depressive psychosis is a relatively common condition in most large mental hospitals. It is so called because the same patient may have periods of excitement or depression separated by phases of apparent well-being. The stage of excitement begins with arrogance, assurance, exuberance and energy, and may super-ficially resemble the pleasantly boisterous drunk seen at a national convention. The patient talks rapidly, histrionically, and with a play on words called "flight of ideas" because each new phrase suggests new ideas on which the patient will embark, leaving the main thought-stream. This excitement may continue to the point where the fatigueless drive is remarkably great. This may or may not be followed by an opposite reaction.

In the depressive phase patients may feel gloomy, speak slowly, and look worried. A feeling of inadequacy may lead to self-punishment and suicidal intent. The symptoms may progress to the complete inactivity known as stupor.

The first manifestation of this disease is usually manic with the first depressive state years later. Attacks last about six months or longer and although they usually recur at a future date, may not. In the time between attacks the patient may appear quiet normal and return to his previous activities.

In the manic phase, sedatives are frequently administered. Stimulating music would only tend to increase the disturbance. If the physician prescribes music it should be of the restful type, preferably a selection which will attract the patient's attention by its familiarity.

In the depressive phase, patients should not hear cheerful and gay music. Entertainment often deepens the depressive state be-cause of the contrast, and the awareness of their own problem, which prevents enjoyment.

Schizophrenia literally means splitting of the mind. It is a group of conditions in which the usual harmonious blending of emotions, intellect, and drive are disorganized into a seeming in-activity and resultant apathy. In the *simple* type the patient be-comes uninterested in his environment and responsibilities. This result is seen in the vagrant and the delinquent.

In the type known as *catatonic* there are phases of excitement or stupor. In the stuporous state the attitude of the patient resembles that of an automaton. In this state it is difficult to make any contact with the patient who refuses to co-operate or even move. Catatonic excitement sometimes follows the stupor and is evidenced by the same purposeless absence of emotion, but may include unexpected acts of destructiveness.

There is another type called *paranoid* in which the patient develops false beliefs of persecution, and a hebephrenic type in which the patient becomes even more inaccessible and inattentive.

Schizophrenia, once thought incurable, is now considered amenable to treatment and about one fourth of the stricken recover completely after the first attack.

In treating these patients an attempt is often made to promote an interest in real things and social consciousness. It is necessary to stimulate attention and redirect it to things outside the patient. Music has a more important place in this disease than in any other mental condition, and this disease may account for more than half the population of many mental hospitals.

Altshuler and Shebesta (4) tried music in the treatment of four excited female schizophrenics in conjunction with hydrotherapy. To have some basis for evaluation of effect, the amount of vocal productions and head movements were recorded for thirty minute periods. This combination is referred to as "output". Observations were made for a six week period, five days a week for two to three hours a day. Two patients were given continuous baths and two were given cold wet sheet packs during the observation periods. A violinist played behind a screen for the first thirty minutes. During the first ten to twenty minutes of playing no changes were noted, and the patients seemed more or less inattentive to the music. Soon it was found that familiar tunes were most effective in centering and keeping their attention. Thus, very noisy and upset patients might begin to sing a familiar song with the violin, keeping their output of energy at the same level but changing from irrelevant purposeless activity to the directed activity of singing or humming a tune. It was also noted that the effect of familiar tunes extended far beyond the termination of the music, as manifested by continued singing after the music stopped. Familiar waltzes were found to be the best type of music to use in quieting the patients, but these were more effective when preceded by more lively tunes which secured their attention.

As a control, patients were placed in dry sheets and after twenty to thirty minutes of music the output diminished in the same degree (50%) that was observed with patients in wet packs. This showed that possibly the music alone may have been responsible for the quieting effect.

These authors conclude that musical accompaniment tends to prevent the feeling that hydriatic measures are punitive and that the return of real memories is a natural substitute for states of phantasy and excitement.

Julia Eby (29) feels that

> "If in the development of a person's talent for music, stress is laid upon the enjoyment it will give further listeners, he is being made conscious of the social significance of his own accomplishments and this helps the development of the personality as a contributing member of the community.

> "Music contributes emotional energy needed to turn dissatisfaction into mental reconstruction. The playing of music arouses associations which stimulate the intellect and if this is sufficient it gives satisfaction and enhances self respect." But "We must

be careful to excite only those activities that will be
followed by a feeling of success".

"The intellectual stimuli of music bring the expenditure of emotional energy from unconscious levels to
conscious and intellectually controlled levels . . . a
concentration on environment stimuli instead of in-
trapsychic impulses, a perseverance in effort to adjust
one's own conduct to group standards."

Altshuler (2) points out that the seat of all sensation, emotion,
and esthetic feeling (the thalamus) is not involved in mental
illness, and is directly attacked by music. The musical stimulation
of the thalamus automatically transfers from this "below awareness" level to the brain cortex.

"Little constructive therapy is possible as long as the
patient is acutely disturbed; therefore anything
which may lessen disturbance and bring about
association familiar to the patient and which will
revive thoughts to a real level will be desirable."

Psychoneurosis differs from psychosis in that the patient recognizes that he is ill and wants to get well, although his more powerful subconcious desire does not. Several types are recognized.

Hysteria is an unconscious reaction on the part of an individual
to solve a personal problem by the acquisition of some symptom
or symptoms. If this is done consciously it is called *malingering*.
Any and every physical or mental symptom is possible. Examples
of physical involvement are blindness, paralysis, aches and pains.
Mental manifestations may include loss of memory, delirium, etc.
Hysteria permits the patient to achieve his purpose and maintain
his self-respect. It is an escape mechanism to evade responsibility,
excuse failure, or gain attention.

Many forms of treatment have been used and each physician uses his own approach. The more commonly accepted methods include psychotherapy, persuasion, suggestion, and psycho-analysis. Psychotherapy encourages the patient to talk about his condition and with the guidance of the psychiatrist discover the basis of his difficulties. Logical persuasion is used but is not considered effective by most. Suggestion under hypnosis is used by some who are expert in hypnotism. Psychoanalysis attempts to discover the subconscious thoughts and experiences which have caused the disturbance.

Music may be of some value for this group. Levine (56) believes that

> "Many individuals achieve a feeling of self-confidence if they develop hobbies such as music. Learning to play musical instruments may compensate a feeling of inferiority, especially when the individual has ability which he underestimates."

Listening to music may stimulate the patient to talk about his condition or about things that trouble him. Altshuler (3) feels that where large groups of patients must be treated with limited personnel, such as exists in hospitals which handle cases of war neuroses, group treatment is the only solution, and that when there is group psychotherapy music is indispensable, for it not only can "turn any aggregation of people into an 'organic' group. It is one of the mightiest socializing agents."

Harrington (43) believes that music has an important place in the mental hospital although he regards technical instruction for heterogenious groups unworthy of the effort. He is convinced that, "Mass singing has therapeutic value, and that subdued instrumental music during mealtimes is desirable."

According to Kraines (54)

"Recreation and hobbies are also extremely important energy release techniques. The apparently passive listening to music may accomplish release of energy. The passivity is only seeming. The person following the music tends by identification to swing muscularly with the music, nodding his head, tapping his feet; and even when there is no manifest movement, there is often a non-observable but yet definite movement. In many forms of music such rhythmic movements can be performed only by relaxed muscles; and tense persons who are influenced by harmonious music are perforce relaxed. Some sanatariums very effectively utilize dancing to music as a means of relaxing patients. Moreover in this general relaxation and harmonious appeal to the senses, the person "feels" that peace and harmony do exist outside himself and will continue to exist despite his own troubles; and by such general "feeling tone", the person puts aside his conflicts for the while. On the other hand some types of music will stimulate persons into increased activity (e.g. martial music, dance music) by reason of the tendency to make rapid and staccato rhythmic movement in time with the music. The rhythmic muscle movement can, under the influence of a skillful composer, increase to such a pitch as to make the person excited, exhilarated, etc. Outlets for energy release should be selected which will give enjoyment to the patient."

In chronic mental institutions the patient band has been found most valuable. Pierce (66) believes that

"Music can be a co-operative effort for a wholesome

discipline. It tends to break down the sense of isola-
tion so common to mental disease. It assists in
adaptation to the mental state.

"First, playing must be made a pleasure to the members. This means there must be no severity of discipline and great tact must be exercised in correcting
errors — preferably privately so as not to be humili-
ating to the patient.

"Second, have some easy numbers: otherwise the results may discourage the patients.
"Public appearances away from the hospital have the
advantages of enhancing self respect and pride.

"Admit a small number of hospital personnel to the
band — but not those of great ability. The more
varied the instrumentation, the more gratifying the
result to the participants."

Mental Deficiency means the incomplete development of the
mind which makes independent living impossible for the victims.
The degrees of deficiency are classified according to the results
obtained in intelligence tests: 1. Idiot — mental age of less than
three years. 2. Imbecile — age of three to seven. 3. Moron —
above the age of eight, but deficient. The treatment for these
groups consists of custodial and hygienic care plus any education
which can be attained, and of course music will play its part in
this in a purely academic manner.

SUMMARY

Music can be used in psychiatry for its value in listening, group
participation, and creation of sound, as follows:

1. *By listening*

    A. To improve attention.
    B. To maintain interest.
    C. To influence mood (to produce exhilaration, etc.).
    D. To produce sedation.
    E. To release energy (by tapping of foot, etc.).

2. *By participation* (in group singing, bands, etc.)

    A. To bring about communal co-operation.
    B. To release energy.
    C. To arouse interest.

3. *By creation of sound* (playing of instruments)

    A. To increase self respect by accomplishment and success.
    B. To increase personal happiness by ability to please others.
    C. To release energy.

CHAPTER FIVE

BACKGROUND MUSIC

The average mind is incapable of engaging effectively in two thought processes simultaneously, but it can in the course of daily routine accept a multitude of mental stimuli at any one moment. If one of these stimuli is sound, it may be the natural complement to the visual experience without which a feeling of incompleteness may result. The observer at the sea-side is intrigued by the cyclic rolling of the waves, and the periodic crashing of the breakers is an integral part of the pleasure of watching waves. Yet, that same series of sounds might be very disturbing to the same person who is trying to work out his income tax return in the quiet of his study. The importance of complementary sound becomes more apparent when one studies the reaction of an audience attending the "movies" during periods of faulty mechanical silence. Sound as a background to mental or physiologic processes may be natural or undesirable but can be very important. If carefully selected, there are few situations in which music cannot be used advantageously as a background to improve the quality or pleasure of activities and living.

At this point it must be repeated that the importance of music in the lives of people is not uniform and that, for those few who dislike music, background music is not recommended.

Background music, as its name implies, is always secondary to some other activity. Only those phases of the subject which touch upon hospital life will be discussed here, and they are, in order of

importance: the music which accompanies meals, painful procedures, calisthenics, and work. Inasmuch as the latter two are
not encountered in all hospitals they will be given only brief consideration. The subject of mealtime music is of sufficient importance to be treated at length and will be discussed in the following
chapter.

Counter-irritation is a very old method of treating pain. For
painful conditions where specific relief can be given in no other
manner, physicians did and still do try to distract the mind from
the site and severity of the pain by transferring attention to
another area. This can be accomplished by irritating the skin
over the affected area in the hope that the resultant inflammation
will be more superficial and visible and in that way neutralize
the pain. In a less physical sense people "take their mind off"
unpleasant subjects by exposure to humor or other forms of
entertainment. Avicenna, the great Bagdad physician (980-1037
A.D.) included in his Canons of Medicine (37) the following
suggestions:

> "1084 . . . Other means of allaying pain: 3. Agree-
> able music, especially if it inclines one to sleep. 4.
> Being occupied with something very engrossing re-
> moves the severity of pain."

Music has been used against pain for centuries not only by
musicians and physicians, but by the people. We find this practice
referred to in a letter from Maria Cosway to Thomas Jefferson
concerning his recently sprained wrist:

> "I wish you were well enough to come to us to-
> morrow . . . I would divert your pain with good
> music (12)."

In 1915 two surgeons named Burdick and Kane used music as

a diversion during local anesthesia. They ascertained the musical preference of the patient prior to operation and played recorded music in muffled tones during the operation. Later they played music in an adjacent room while general anesthesia was being induced and found that it was accomplished with less resistance (32). Since that time other surgeons have used music for similar purposes. There are some operations which are done under local anesthesia and are prolonged. The absence of sounds other than awe-inspiring whispers, or the presence of technical talk may cause the patient unnecessary alarm.

The use of well selected music or a good radio program may be of great benefit in the operating room. Its value will depend upon the operating surgeon and how well he can operate while music is being played. There are times during an operation when delicate maneuvers become trying and the wrong music or increased volume might lead to exasperation. One advocate of music in the operating room has called it a "psychic anesthetic" (53).

The use of local anesthetics in dentistry has made possible the painless extraction of teeth. Most dentists, however, do not inject local anesthetics before drilling cavities. For many people, drilling is a frightful experience. Some dentists have advocated the playing of music at a loud level during this procedure. Still another has incorporated ear-phones into the head rest of the dental chair for diversional sound.

A more obvious use of diversional sound in the professional office is in the reception or waiting room to supplement the magazines and diminish the terror of waiting. Music may also be used during such time-consuming treatment as physical therapy, deep x-ray therapy, and fever-therapy.

PHYSICAL EXERCISE

Some forms of physical exercise are carried out most successfully when accompanied by music. Plato recommended such a practice in his *Republic*. In the ancient triremes or boats with three banks of oars, there was always a tibicen or flute player, not only to keep uniform rhythm among the workmen, but to sooth and cheer them. From this custom Quintillian took occasion to say that music enables us more patiently to support toil and labor (15).

During the Six-Day Bicycle Race at the Madison Square Garden in 1911 forty-six mile races were separately timed on three evenings; half were ridden to music. The average time with music was 19.6 miles per hour, and without it only 17.9 (5).

Tarchanoff found that

"if the fingers are completely fatigued, either by
voluntary effort or by electric excitation, music has
the power of making fatigue disappear." (74)

Such an observation leaves little doubt that physical endeavor is more productive when done to music.

Calisthenics. This is not the place to discuss the value of calisthenics or its use in hospitals. Exercise has come to be considered the important physical conditioner, and calisthenics is the universally practiced exercise. Its proper performance will depend upon the ability of the leader, the willingness of the participants and the ingenuity expended to make it interesting. The willingness of the group can be enhanced by large numbers of performers, but under any circumstances, since it is unproductive and involves work, any adjunct which will increase interest is welcome. The exponents of both the Swedish and the German systems of calisthenics claim equally good results, but the former do not use any musical accompaniment, whereas some schools in Germany, particularly the one at Hellerau, make extensive use of it. In fact, Dalcroze and his followers have built an entire philosophy of esthetics called "Eurhythmics" based upon the relationship between body motion and music.

Unproductive exercise can undoubtedly be made more interesting by musical accompaniment. Music can regulate the orderliness of action by relating the sense of hearing to the sense of muscular movement.

Johnson (51) believed that the strength of muscle contraction increases with the intensity and pitch of accompanying music, and that the point of fatigue is postponed when calisthenics is given to music, but that unsteadiness might result from variation in the musical score. Anything that will divert the attention from the proper execution of the exercise is a hindrance, and music should not be used until the exercise has become thoroughly mastered. Once the exercise has become second nature, music becomes very useful because it acts as a stimulus and adds interest.

It is difficult to move rhythmically out of time with the music. Most popular recorded music is in a tempo too rapid to be satisfactory for calisthenics. For this reason live music is far more satisfactory as an accompaniment, and a single instrument, preferable the piano, is most suited to it. The pianist can take the cue from the exercise leader for tempo. The piano should be played in a steady unvarying rhythmic style. Well known tunes and folksongs should be used. The piano must be played loud and with strongly accentuated rhythm. Hulbert (49) relied largely on waltzes, marches, and folk-songs played slowly. The songs he used to advantage include "Believe Me If All Those Endearing Young Charms," "Bonnie Dundee" and "O No, John." In this country such songs as "The Skater's Waltz" and "There's a Long, Long Trail A Winding" are popular for this use.

Ideally, live music should be used to accompany exercise so that the tempo can be readily adjusted to the speed of the participants. If commercial recordings must be used they should be carefully selected to rule out those containing vocal or other interludes which break up the continuity of the rhythmic pattern, and the operator should silence the machine between successive exercises.

The use of music during exercises will depend upon the value attached to it by the instructor. Some may find the time and trouble required unwarranted. Others may find in it a way to get better co-operation or increased pleasure. There is one use of music in connection with group exercise which is strongly recommended. Preceding the actual period of exercise the playing of a stirring march, while the participants march to their places of assemble, acts as a stimulant and conditioner for the activity to follow.

REMEDIAL EXERCISE AND DANCING

When one or more groups of muscles have become weakened as a result of misuse or disease, it is proper to engage them in strengthening gymnastics called remedial exercises. Although these can frequently be given to groups, the groups are ordinarily small. The nature of these exercises and their administration may lead to boredom rapidly. Soft music can be used as an antidote to their monotony. Those exercises for the correction of spinal deformity which require crawling and free swinging are well adapted to musical accompaniment, and exercise in the form of the dance used for correction or maintenance of good posture is undoubtedly enhanced by background music.

Although not in common use for such purpose, ballroom and tap-dancing could be used to advantage in selected groups of patients for the improvement of disabilities of the ankles, knees and hips. Modern or interpretative dancing may in like manner be used for upper extremity strengthening and co-ordination.

SHOP WORK

In those hospitals which possess an occupational therapy shop, music may be used to increase the pleasantness of the surroundings and possibly to increase the endurance and efficiency of work projects.

Music is not recommended as a background to work which requires mental concentration, even though it is used by a great many students who believe that they can do their home-work better with the radio on. If the melody is too interesting or too popular at the time, it may be distracting, but where the work is largely physical, soft music has been shown to be a desirable adjuvant. Gatewood (33) studied the effect of background music on workers in an architectural drafting room and discovered that although a minority found it distracting, most of the workers worked better and faster. They preferred familiar music and found instrumental music less distracting than vocal renditions.

More recently this subject has received the attention of many investigators who have shown its value among factory workers and have called it "Industrial Music."* Their findings and conclusions are so closely allied with the use of background music that a few excerpts from the growing literature will be mentioned.

Beckett (9) analyzed the reports made by those factories which have been broadcasting music to their employes through public address systems. There was improved morale in every plant where

---

* The use of industrial music is not to be confused with working songs. Working songs are those sung by groups performing tedious or strenuous work to help them maintain good rhythm and spirit. Bücher (Bücher, K., Arbeit und Rhythmus, Leipzig, 1909) analyzed a long list of working songs and concluded that: 1. Through rhythm they facilitate the synchronous expenditures of energy by individuals engaged in a common task. 2. They spur the worker on through jest, abuse, or reference to the spectators' opinions. 3. They mention the work, its progress, pleasures, vexations, difficulties and rewards. 4. They inform everyone of the wishes and aspirations of the workers. These slow rhythmic songs are entirely unsuited to the machine age where the machine sets the inelastic rhythm for the worker.

the music lasted for at least one hour daily. Two-thirds of the factories which played music for at least one hour on each shift claimed an increase in production of from five to ten percent. Greater efficiency results from using music to relieve the boredom of repetitive operations, to reduce nervous tension, to take the workers mind off himself, and in general to make the shop a more attractive place in which to work. He finds the evidence undeniable that music can increase production, but points out that this result will depend upon how the project is managed. If the acoustics or mechanical reproduction is poor, the value of music may be lost. The most important short-coming at present is the difficulty in obtaining suitable commercial recordings. Because of the noise in the average plant, the volume of the music must be slightly greater than that produced by the machines. But the average recording has such fluctuations in volume that some parts will be drowned out by the hum of the work and other sections will be too loud. Ideally, recordings for industrial music should vary only slightly in volume, from "plus or minus two decibels of tone intensity", and these are not available in variety at present.

"The kind of music played is of paramount importance, but no one type of music can be used exclusively without becoming a bore to the listener. When request boxes are installed, it is often the young and enthusiastic 'jive fans' who use them to the fullest, while the more conservative music lovers usually sit back and take what comes. Sometimes this has led to the mistaken view that the whole plant desired the more raucous music. After a trial of this type of music some firms received unfavorable reports on production and lost faith in music. In some instances music was then abandoned altogether, whereupon there was such an outcry from the workers that the program was reinstated with hot swing entirely eliminated. Both extremes are bad. Giving the workers what they want is a more difficult problem than it appears at first.

It requires not one but a number of questionnaires over a period of time to keep up with changing tastes."

"Music must be played at the right time to obtain the best results. Marches create a cheerful atmosphere and should be played at the beginning of sessions, as well as at the end. The best time of the day for Strauss waltzes is at the so-called 'fatigue periods.' There is something about three-quarter time that is very refreshing at moments of fatigue. Besides the music is gay and light-hearted, and leads all other forms in popular appeal according to questionnaires filled in at three large plants."

In the hospital occupational therapy shop, music may originate from the public address system, a record player, or the radio. It would seem that the most suitable in the average hospital would be the use of the radio, which the therapist can change at intervals of fifteen minutes or longer in an attempt to get unexciting music at a low volume level.

CHAPTER SIX

MEALTIME MUSIC

Patients who are confined to bed, or for that matter, to a hospital, find meals progressively monotonous in spite of the fact that there is a greater variety offered them than was theirs at home. This monotony results in part from the color and nature of the environment, the personnel, the general atmosphere of the hospital, and the constraining nature of institutional restriction. While dining at home some of these factors are subconsciously dissipated by trivial intimate conversation, friendly faces, individual attention and the security of the things for which "home" stands.

There are only a few things which can be done to make hospital meals more enjoyable, aside from those features best handled by the chef and menu planner; but it is possible to increase the pleasure of meal periods through the manipulation of certain environmental factors. One of these is the use of color and *decor* in hospital dining halls to simulate home surroundings. In the ward this is most difficult where little can be done, except by introducing attractive hangings which are less hospital-like, or by the application of paint in cheerful colors. The latter method is sanitary and practical.

Since ancient times music has been used as an accompaniment to meals. The instruments used by the ancients for this purpose were usually those which emitted soft sounds. Voltaire said that our purpose in going to the opera was to promote digestion. During the preceding century, dinner music became stylized and consisted largely of semi-classical pieces or waltzes played softly in slow tempo by string ensembles. During the past twenty-five years there has evolved a form of dinner music which is not only a marked departure from the old, but has come to be used as a source for dancing between and during courses. Whether the physiologic and psychologic effects of dancing during a meal are harmful, beneficial, or of no moment remains undecided. Certainly there seems to have been little interest in analyzing its effects. During the period when dinner-dance music was available only in a few places, the number of those who could be affected by it was very small. But, with the more recent installations of "juke" boxes, and other forms of mechanically reproduced music, into all varieties of dining places, the problem is worthy of investigation.

Most people derive pleasure from the consumption of appetizing food. Most people derive pleasure from music played to their taste. Although the logic of the following thought is subject to criticism, it does sound reasonable to state that two pleasurable experiences enjoyed simultaneously, should add up to a greater happiness than that afforded by either individually. Food has received thorough study with respect to preservation, preparation, serving, and the time of day when each item is most satisfying. Some of the conclusions have been arbitrary, but for the most part, people eat the food that agrees with them physiologically and psychologically. There is no especially good reason why cereals should be eaten by adults only in the morning. It has become a matter of custom or advertising, and the minds of the masses have become conditioned to feel that cereal is especially good at breakfast time. A generation ago the breakfast menu in some homes differed little from the present day dinner fare. Eating habits have become set in the minds of most people and there is little that can be done to change them rapidly. Daily routines have given rise to certain music conventions as well. Until recently, music at breakfast was uncommon. Bernard Shaw (65) wrote, "Music after dinner is pleasant: Music before breakfast is so unpleasant as to be clearly unnatural." With the advent of radio this has changed even if Shaw has not. Lunch rooms, barbershop and other public places where people spend time inactively, are equipped with mechanisms for reproducing music. The practice of reading or even studying school work at home with the radio on has become increasingly prevalent. The tempo of living has stepped up to the point where most people, especially the younger, like to do two things at once, especially if one of these is to listen to music.

The effect of different foods upon digestion and health is known, and most persons eat with a regularity which is related to capacity and needs. They are usually able to select the items they desire, the time at which they will eat, and the period for consumption.

The ideal attitude while eating is one of mental serenity and physical repose. If certain criteria are observed music can be relaxing. The elements which increase relaxation are melody, rhythm, and softness. If the music which accompanies meals is carefully selected it can make eating more pleasurable, and this is desirable for patients in the hospital.

Mealtime music must be unobtrusive. It must lack stimulating qualities which attract attention. If the diner can promptly name the selection played five minutes earlier, that piece was too impressive in score or performance. Perhaps the most suitable form of dinner music is that played by a small string ensemble. The piano and harp are also very satisfactory, alone or in combination with the ensemble. When the piano is played in the hesitant legato style of Eddie Duchin it is particularly desirable. The shrill sounds of the flute or the brassy sound of the trumpet must be omitted. The music must be soft and slow. Avoid vocals and strange instruments.

The volume of the music should be maintained at as nearly the same level as is consistent with the source of the music. It should begin without fanfare or any attempt to attract attention. The level of intensity should not interfere with conversation, for, if the loudness of the music demands an increased volume of voice to carry on normal conversation, it defeats the purpose of relaxation by evoking increased energy on the part of the speaker. When possible the end of the selection should fade out. There should be nothing abrupt about the selection, and unusual sequences or novelties should be avoided. The music should be fluent and entirely unexciting. The interval between pieces should be brief in order to sustain auditory reception at a fairly continuous level. Five to ten seconds between numbers is recommended, and this coincides approximately with the time required to change discs on an automatic or manually controlled record player. Musical selections should be played in groups. The groups should last a total of about fifteen minutes with rest intervals of about three minutes. This simulates the requirements and performance of the live ensemble and has become a part of stylized dinner music. The music should last as long as the meal.

Ideally, the source of the music should not be obvious, and to this end a concealed loud speaker has an advantage over the live ensemble, which through its motions or the physical appearance or mannerisms of its members may distract diners. There should be no vocal announcements between selections. Occasionally a listener will want to know the name of the song being played because it is familiar, reminiscent, or sweet. When the budget will permit, printed or mimeographed programs are most welcome to those whose interest is aroused.

The music recommended, is the music which has been played

by dinner ensembles for years. Their repertoires usually include waltzes by Strauss and his contemporaries; selections from operettas by Herbert, Friml, and Romberg, and the popular favorites of the past decade, such as selections from the musical comedies of Kern, Cole Porter and Gershwin, or the songs of Carmichael and Berlin.

It cannot be emphasized too strongly that mealtime music must be physiologically non-stimulating, and noisy music is to be avoided. "Douglas Jerrold declared that he hated to dine amidst the strains of a military band; he said he could taste the brass in his soup." (Hadden, J., *"Music as Medicine,"* 1895, 9:369). A foreman of a shop in which music was played during mealtime begged that raucous music be omitted "to give the digestion a break" (9).

Some orchestra leaders habitually use arrangements which approximate the qualities desirable for mealtime music. Among these are: Wayne King, Marek Weber, Andre Kostelanetz, David Rose, Frankie Carle, Carmen Cavallaro, Eddie Duchin, Guy Lombardo, and the following orchestras: Boston "Pops", New Mayfair, Percy Faith, Anton and Paramount, Victor Salon, Victor Continental, Palmer House Ensemble, Selinsky String Ensemble. All these have been recorded and a sample list of their recordings follows as a nucleus of a mealtime music library.

Victor Recordings

Southern Roses	26322 B
Sweetheart Waltz	26322 A
Black Eyes	20037 B
Our Waltz	27853 B
Holiday for Strings	27853 B
Frühlingstimmen	4387 A and B
Dream Waltz	V 214

None But The Lonely Heart	4413 B
Song of The Islands	27224 B
La Golondrina	27451 B
Lover, Come Back To Me	27397 A
Indian Love Call	27397 B
Le Secret	20416 A
Pirouette	20416 B
Wine, Women And Song	6647 A
A Shepherd's Tale	9479 A
Narcissus	9479 B
Come Back To Sorrento	27917 A
Cavotte from Mignon	27917 B
Zigeuner	24609 B
Tales of Hoffman	20011 B
Badinage	12591 A
Air de Ballet	12591 B
Gold and Silver	25199 B
Blue Danube	25199 A

Columbia Recordings

Begin the Beguine	4265 M
Easter Parade	4292 M
With A Song In My Heart	4292 M
The Touch Of Your Hand	4291 M
Somebody Loves Me	4291 M
Falling In Love	4266 M
Tea For Two	4266 M
Josephine	36692
Louise	36692
Estrellita	4236 M
London Again	69264 D
By The Tamarisk	69264 D
Swan Lake	69357 D

Rosalie	36543
Speak To Me Of Love	35551
Pavanne	7361 M
Clair De Lune	7361 M

Decca Recordings

The Very Thought Of You	3110 B
Cocktails For Two	3110 A
Every Little Movement	18300 B
Minute Waltz	18466 A
Blue September	15050 A
Valse Bluette	15049 B
Sleepy Lagoon	18286 A

CHAPTER SEVEN

MUSIC IN BED

Modern hospitals are so different in organization and equipment from what they were a century ago, that it may be said that the hospital is a recently acquired phase of community life. Originally, the sick were treated in their own homes. The inconveniences and inadequacies of caring for the seriously, and especially the contagiously, ill at home led to the development of hospitals. The primary purpose of the hospital has not changed, and the musical aide must never forget that medical care and rest come before all else.

Some bed patients are too ill to listen to music. It is possible that judiciously offered music might be of value to all patients but it is safer to deny a few in the absence of expert medical guidance than to disturb the sick. The musical aide may not question the wisdom of the physician in prohibiting the use of music in some wards or for some patients. The physician knows many things about the patient which are unknown to the musician and there is insufficient time to explain these to the musician. In institutions where the public-address system distributes music through earphones rather than through loud speakers, listening presents no problem and head-phones are not supplied to patients until the physician permits it. When only loud speakers are available, and the ward houses a mixture of seriously ill and convalescent patients (as is fairly common in large public hospitals) it may be necessary to deprive the ward of music for the sake of the few who should not have it.

The number of possibilities which may be found on any one ward is so great that only the most general kinds of use will be mentioned. Pediatric wards are frequently arranged so that the acutely ill are segregated, and this permits ward music at most times. Where patients are intermixed, the attending physician will make the decision. The importance of scheduling for children is enhanced by the fact that most children prefer their music loud, and this can be especially annoying to the sicker children. As a general rule it might be stated that with the progress from childhood to old age, the preference shifts from fast loud high-pitched music to softer and slower music. The speaker volume on the pediatric ward may be increased to gain the attention of some children, and drown out the crying of others. Children can listen to the same set of records almost endlessly. They prefer to hear music with which they are acquainted. They like songs with words.

One reason for hospitalization is to get the patient away from the annoyances and noises of home. One of the modern noises is the radio. Most patients sleep and need more sleep than well people. In most hospitals certain hours of the day are chosen for rest in the hope that the patients will fall asleep. The usual period for daytime slumber is directly after lunch. The filling of the stomach is in itself a soporific. Warmth, darkness, and physical relaxation increase the tendency to sleep. Since there is no universally sleep-inducing music, music should be avoided at this time. It may keep some awake. If the patient is in a private room and is willing to be played to sleep it should be attempted. It must be remembered that if the music is sufficiently interesting or if the reproduction is poor or scratchy it may prolong wakefulness or even prevent sleep.

At those times when slumber music is requested by the physician or the patient, a few common sense rules should be followed. For children vocal lullabies should be tried. Slumber music should not be played for more than fifteen minutes. If it has not been effective in that period, silence is indicated.

Admission to a hospital usually means new eating and sleeping habits for the patient. The hours for each are frequently earlier than previously. Day-time naps and early "lights out" make it difficult for some to fall asleep promptly at night for the first few nights. Slumber music should take the form of restful music. The final fifteen minutes of the day should be given over to sweet melodies of old time favorites which may recall old pleasant memories and possibly place the patient in a "dreamy" mood of relaxation removed from the specious present and its worries. The operator of the sound control should gradually and imperceptibly reduce the volume so that the final moments are barely audible.

In hospitals equipped with "radio-pillows" in which telephones are concealed within the pillows, the music may remain continuous until the patient falls asleep. Many people have developed the habit of falling asleep to radio music or turning it off when they become sleepy. Radio programs are not recommended as slumber music. The musical program should use the old favorites or, meal-time music selections (See Chapter VI) at a very low volume. Loud and stirring music before bed-time has been known to result in vivid auditory dreams, and should be avoided. (24)

The Bedside Radio

More than any other single factor, the radio has increased musical knowledge and appreciation in this country. The programs of Bing Crosby and Alec Templeton have great popular appeal because of the extensive preparation, humor, and showmanship contained in them. Yet these programs never fail to include classical music, and introduce serious music to those who would not freely choose to listen to it. But more than any other single factor, the improper use of the bedside radio can make patients hate music. The most passionate lovers of music will admit that it is possible to have too much music of the same kind for peaceful consumption. In hospitals with large wards, two or more radios may be found tuned in to different programs, and the desire to share the program with others means excessive volume. In those institutions which do not possess a public address system radios should be permitted on the wards but certain rules should be observed. The volume should be controlled so that patients who are not interested do not have to suffer. The volume should be one that makes the signal just audible to the owner and to those of his neighbors who wish to listen. For several hours of the day interludes of silence should be observed by all owners of radios. In hospitals with a loud-speaker system, all radios should be turned off during the hours of its operation.

In hospitals for the chronically ill, such as tuberculosis sanatoria, where the musical tastes on the ward may run a wide gamut, a schedule should be arranged for those possessing radios, alloting certain periods of the day to each owner and arranging the sound distribution so that two or more radios may be turned on simultaneously but spaced so far apart that the resulting sound will not result in a form of punishment for those caught in between or not fortunate enough to own their own radios.

After "lights out" radios frequently remain on unless supervision is severe. It is true that many of the better programs are heard after nine o'clock. Since some of the late programs are part of American life, it is unfair to the chronically ill to deprive them of this well planned entertainment. Yet there will be some on the ward who will want to sleep, and they should be given maximum consideration. Others should be permitted to keep their radios on at the lowest possible volume, and the possibility of headphone installations should be reviewed. The solution to this problem is possible but expensive. If a record-cutting device is available, the program may be recorded at night and replayed on the following day.

PUBLIC ADDRESS SYSTEM

Many hospitals have already been equipped with either loud-speaker or headphone installations. For those hospitals which are still in the deciding stage, some of the advantages of each will be briefly considered.

Ideally, both speakers and head-phones should be available. This is a luxury in which few will be willing or able to indulge. When head-phones are used, they have a way of getting misplaced, broken or broken-down. Head-phones or listening devices are usually distributed to those patients who are medically eligible. Frequently the attendants are busy and forget to supply them, to the chagrin of the patient. When there are not enough to go around a further source of dissatisfaction arises. Head-phones must be adjusted for proper reception and comfort, and this may become a source of bother to patients or staff. Among the advantages of 'phones are the quietness of wards at all times for those who desire rest. Their use permits maximum focusing of attention on the music because of the exclusion of most other sounds. They become a mechanism of escape from the unwanted conversation of noisome neighbors. When double-jacks or two-channel wiring is used the patient is permitted some choice in music selection. The use of 'phones, however, limits the physical excursion of the ambulatory patient.

The use of a loud-speaker system permits those patients not strictly confined to their beds to visit other parts of the ward without interruption in their listening. Some patients enjoy music as a background to conversation or ward activities. The same switchboard may be used for musical programs and hospital announcement, and this may be desirable economically in some institutions. Strategically placed speakers may be channeled exclusively as a call system.

Laughter is a communal reaction. We rarely react completely to a radio joke if we are listening alone, but if several people listen simultaneously laughter becomes more pronounced and prolonged. Loud-speaker systems permit patients on the ward to enjoy music as a group. They also permit the greater use of background music. Eating with the encumbrance of head-phones is not desirable.

Each hospital will have to weigh these and other arguments of the speaker - phone dilemma and choose according to its individual requirements.

The most suitable number of channels for a small hospital is two. One operator can readily handle two channels. When the number of channels is increased above this the expense of installation and operation will increase, especially if recordings or transcriptions are to be used in addition to outside programs.

The operator of the public address system should be conversant with the Hooper or Crossley ratings of the more important programs and be certain to include the most popular at any one hour in re-broadcast.

PERSONALIZED MUSIC

The more musically inclined or susceptible patient may not be satisfied with the routine musical program as furnished by the public address system or even his radio. In hospitals where the majority taste is for modern popular music, there will be a few who will hunger for classical. If a musical aide is available this may be accomplished by the use of a music cart. A box-like device on wheels such as is used for many purposes on hospital wards may be fitted with a record player and a rack for records and record albums. The music cart may carry some small instruments and other materials for bedside use. Music can be wheeled to the bedside for instruction, appreciation, diversion, or entertainment.

Instruction. Bedside instruction may be used as occupational therapy or for purely educational purposes. Small instruments such as the ukelele, mandolin, or even the guitar may be taught to the bed patient as upper extremity exercise. Instrumental instruction will usually have to be limited to patients in individual rooms. Occasionally wards will be arranged so that a day-room or sun porch is available for wheel chair or partially restricted patients, and there will be times when the patient may receive instruction there. There are some instruments which may be played with a minimum of instruction. Unfortunately most of these emit sounds which are quite annoying to all but the performer. The ocarina and harmonica may meet with some acceptance among young patients, but when older patients share the ward or adjoining room their feelings will have to come first. Some young patients will delight in the use of drum sticks on practice blocks, especially if they can use them during the reproduction of music on the public address system or the radio. If the block is made of rubber or some other noiseless material it will not be too annoying to neighboring patients.

Specially constructed "toneless" or "practice" instruments such as the violin without the resonator are of genuine value in diminishing neighbor annoyance. These may be built in the occupational therapy shop from discarded instruments.

Diversion. For those who desire diversion and music appreciation, the music aide may wheel the music cart to the bedside. By ascertaining the musical appetite of patients on the preceding day, the aide may stock the cart with the kind of recordings desired and play them for the interested patient and any of the neighboring patients whose interest she can stimulate. By making a few well chosen remarks before each record is played much interest can be developed and the patient will look forward to future visits. If patients express no special interest in music, albums may be passed out for browsing and played without predetermined continuity. If interest is greatly aroused the music aide may suggest supplemental reading and call on the librarian to visit the patient or supply some reading material from the music department collection. The commercially available program notes for sponsored radio programs should also be distributed.

Entertainment. Musical entertainment on the ward may take the form of patient participation or "live" music. For patient participation, there is nothing to equal ward sings. The music aide may use either the record-player in the music cart or, preferably, a portable instrument such as a small piano organ, or accordion. The words of the songs may be mimeographed or flashed on a screen, wall, or ceiling with a small projector. Hymn books or other books of songs may also be used to advantage. Songs should be chosen for their popularity and familiarity. Such songs as "Let Me Call You Sweetheart" and other old favorites are "sure fire". The top songs on the "Hit Parade" are always enjoyed. The music aide should circulate if recorded music is used to stimulate non-participants into singing. The session should last from twenty to thirty minutes. It is desirable to have two of these per ward each week. Duration and frequency can be varied according to patient response.

Of all forms of ward music, good "live" music is perhaps the most entertaining. Ensembles may be of fair quality but soloists must not be mediocre or the presentation will suffer. The most popular entertainers are the singers who can accompany themselves on the portable piano or other instruments. They should keep the program at the popular-appeal level. They should not ask for requests unless their repertoire is adequate since the inability to grant them is both disappointing and embarrassing to both performer and patients.

Volunteers. It will be difficult for one music aide to carry out a music program by himself in a hospital of more than 500 beds. If the budget does not permit a second aide volunteers from the community should be enlisted to assist. This subject will be discussed further in the next chapter.

CHAPTER EIGHT

DIVERSION AND ENTERTAINMENT

A program of musical entertainment is not needed at all hospitals, nor for all patients. Entertainment is relatively new in hospitals. A need for it arose when hospitals for the chronically ill became greater in numbers and size. The average person soon becomes bored when restricted to bed or even the confining walls of an institution. Reading becomes tiresome for most because of position, eye-strain, or satiation. Similar limitations exist to a lesser degree for craftwork. There is a diminution in contact with the outside world except for the too infrequent and short visits of friends or relatives. In hospitals for the tuberculous adult or the crippled child, the average duration of hospitalization may be a year. Few leave before a period of three months and some remain for years. Life for the chronically hospitalized patient may become more monotonous than is wise. Monotony leads to discontent, irritability, apathy, and possibly disciplinary problems. Monotony may make meals even less attractive than they are in some hospitals. Lack of mental occupation may lead to a loss of desire to get well or give the patient too much time to think about himself, his helplessness and hopelessness. Most patients arrive at the point where they crave amusement, and most of them would rather be amused than work for their own entertainment.

In the field of entertainment, music is indispensable. In hospitals, music is frequently the only form of entertainment. Music can be used at the bedside, in the ward, the assembly hall, or when weather permits, outdoors. In hospitals equipped with public address systems the problem is decreased by the simultaneous performance of mechanically reproduced music throughout the wards and rooms of the hospital. Where public address systems have not been installed, entertainment will depend largely on radios, record reproducers, and personal appearances of musicians.

"Live" musicians are the most welcome source of entertainment. If the hospital has a music aide, this aim is partially fulfilled by his activities. If there is no full time musician, hospitals may be able to secure the part-time services of a musician or recreational aide. Some one person should have control of arranging programs, and an interested person will usually be found on the hospital staff. It may be an occupational therapist, a nurse, or even one of the physicians. The person selected to direct music will have little difficulty in finding in the community some musicians or groups of amateur entertainers who will be willing to assist in this work. Groups from schools of music, high schools, fraternal or benevolent organizations, women's clubs, music clubs and veteran's societies constitute an incomplete list of sources. Most communities have soloists or small groups which will be willing to perform. Direct solicitation by the hospital director, the ladies auxiliary, or members of the staff should be made personally or through the press.

A schedule of performances arranged for at least one month in advance is most important. There should be a regularity to performances even if they occur only once a month. It will give patients something to which they may look forward with the pleasure of anticipation. Whenever, possible, musical programs should be prepared for the same weekday or night. These appearances should be announced or posted to increase the interest.

In hospitals for the chronically ill there is usually an assembly hall or recreational building, where entertainment may be given for ambulatory patients. The appearance of famous musicians on its stage will be rare or impossible, especially in hospitals not located near large cities. This is not as unfortunate as might be believed, because although some patients are impressed with names of national reputation, maximum enjoyment will result for the majority from listening to their fellow patients performing. Patient participation is always more desirable for the ambulatory than passive entertainment. Patient music may take one of three forms — formal, amateur, or spontaneous.

Formal presentations require much work on the part of the musical aide and the patients. Orchestras of variable size may be formed, depending upon the number and variety of talented patients. Inasmuch as quality of performance is the prime consideration, the repertoire of such groups will not be great. At the outset it will take almost a month to develop a one hour variety program. With the progress of time and increased work and co-operation it should be possible to rehearse enough new numbers each week to produce a weekly program with too few repetitions to arouse complaints on the part of the patients. The program should contain all types of music so that during the course of a performance almost everyone in the audience will have heard something to his taste. Vocal numbers are welcome and audience participation at one or two points will sustain interest. It is advisable for some one to act as master of ceremonies to announce selections and to evoke maximum response from the non-participating patients. There is usually one patient with a desire to be a master of ceremonies and, if he executes his work well, this will be a valuable asset to the project. A master of ceremonies is important and if necessary an outsider should be secured for this purpose.

Amateur programs have been present on the American scene for a long time but the efforts of Major Bowes have made them an American institution. People of almost all ages will attend them joyfully, but the performers will usually be in the second and third quarters of life's span. There was a time when amateur performances were unrehearsed or sounded so. Major Bowes has changed that, too. The amateur show will now be found to demand rehearsals, expert accompaniment, and a certain amount of theatrical display. These factors should be encouraged and the music aide will do well to humor patients along, because success depends upon the seriousness, energy, and efforts of the performer. Care should be expended in careful programming. The best performers should be well spaced and appear in the second half of the program. Instrumentalists should be separated by vocalists. The procedure should follow the set pattern of regular amateur shows, including the award of prizes to the winner and second best. Where patient turn-over is slow, it is likely that the same performer may be first too often. Some limit should be set on the frequency or total number of times the same patient may receive an award to prevent participation from diminishing.

Spontaneous shows in the recreation hall will consist of community singing, humming, whistling, and occasional rhythmic hand-clapping. It is not difficult to get a group to sing but maximum response will call for ingenuity on the part of the leader. The series of motion picture shorts called "The Bouncing Ball", "Community Sing", and others of a similar nature are excellent because they are complete packages of music, words, direction, humor, and tricks. The song leader should adopt as many of the novelties included in these films as the facilities will allow. Next best to the motion picture is the lantern slide. There are a few available with humorous illustrations, but they may be difficult to obtain. Lantern slides may be made rapidly and inexpensively by the music aide. The makings of simple slides may be had in any large commercial photography supply shop. "Radio Mats" are slide-sized pieces of clear cellophane enclosed in a folded piece of carbon paper and surrounded by a black mask. The "Mat" is placed in a typewriter and the words of the song are typed on it. The carbonized paper is discarded, as is the back of the mask, and the cellophane with words imprinted is easily mounted between the two glass cover-slips joined by "Scotch Tape". By this method a permanent slide may be produced for about eight cents. If a projector is not available, the words may be mimeographed, printed in the occupational therapy shop, or obtained commercially printed in pamphlet form. The salient need is that all may be permitted to read the words.

Community sings should not last too long. The music aide will soon learn to sense the capacity of the audience. To extend the period, patient participation may be interrupted by instrumental music or some other form of interlude.

CHOIR

Listening to a combination of trained voices is pleasurable to most people. Where the patient population is relatively static, the music aide will be well repaid by time spent on training quartettes or larger groups of singers. Such groups can be of value not only in any of the musical programs for the assembly hall but may be used on the wards, for religious services and on holiday occasions. If, as is usual, both sexes are represented among the patients, the range of selections will be limited only by the musicianship of the leader and the participants. The range of repertoire should be suited to all occasions and tastes from "barber-shop" quartets to serious music.

All possible arrangements of voices should be exploited with a view to competitive singing between sexes and among wards. The range of usefulness of this activity will of course depend to a large extent on the size of the hospital and the predominant age group.

Diversion

Music may also be used to help time pass less noticeably. Listening is enjoyable but does not focus or sustain attention in any way comparable to playing. There will always be patients interested in learning to play music. The instrument of choice will depend upon individual taste, which of course is conditioned by background, education, nationality, age, and many other factors. The instruments which will be most acceptable are those which are not too difficult to play and which emit a pleasant sound with ease for a long period.

The piano is the instrument which best meets the qualifications of the ideal instrument for hospital use. When reduced to pure physics, the sound produced by striking a single note on the same keyboard will be of approximately the same quality whether made by a child or a virtuoso. This is not true of any other instruments, except to a degree in certain other percussion instruments, that produce less pleasant or interesting sounds. Piano fingering is more easily mastered than that of stringed instruments, and offers greater latitude in precision placement. The piano may be played in the restful sitting position and requires little effort to play. More people know how to play the piano than any other instrument. Patients may be interested in any of the other instruments, but with the exception of the plectrum type, may become too readily discouraged at the amount of practice required to elicit pleasant tones. If a patient is interested in learning an instrument for diversion, the piano should be the first offered. If the problem of replacing musicians in or completing a patient band arises, the missing instrument should be offered. But in order to get the maximum co-operation and application, the patient should be made to feel that the choice is his. The free choice might be vocal instruction. It may even be a disappointment to the musician when it turns out to be so-called instruments like the ocarina, but if the aim is diversion a maximum will be reached earliest by initial gratification. Perhaps at a later date the music aide may be able to inculcate enough sophistication to lead to the choice of a more musical instrument.

The scope of music as an educational diversion will expand in proportion to the training, patience and energy of the music aide. It will be limited by the number of patients who demonstrate an interest and also upon their intelligence and perseverance. For the major instruments, instruction is usually individual and much time is consumed in the diversion of a single patient. In a large hospital this will not be very practical unless there is a large staff, and there are many activities available to patients. Group diversion can be happily attained by some form of instruction in music appreciation. The nature of this instruction should be tailored to the intelligence and taste of the majority and the music aide must exercise common sense and free himself of prejudice. If the patients are young and uninterested in the classics he must devise a program around popular music and discuss current personalities and popular forms. A driving wedge into the classics may be constructed on the classic themes of Tschaikowsky, Chopin and others which are currently popular. If the group is very young, music appreciation demonstrations such as those conducted by Walter Damrosch should be followed. Whenever possible, the musician should illustrate with "live" music, but recordings will be well received. As with all other features of a musical program in the hospital, sessions should be regular and governed to some extent by the will of the majority.

CHAPTER NINE

PUBLIC ADDRESS SYSTEM

Many hospitals now have public address systems. Before long most hospitals of one hundred or more beds will have public address systems, if for no other reason than emergency calls and to lessen the load on the intramural telephone network.

The public address system originally installed as an emergency call device may be used for music reproduction at relatively little increase in expense. The same operator may be used for both forms of transmission. Ideally, the system should include a loud speaker in every ward and a "phone-jack" at every bedside. The central switchboard should have a good radio and an automatic record player which may transmit music to the patients by means of the public address systems. The addition of a set of switches which can cut wards in or out at will can prove most useful. If there are halls or buildings from which programs of general interest emanate frequently, they should be equipped with microphones which are connected with the central switchboard so that musical programs from the assembly hall or the church services from the chapel may be broadcast to the non-ambulatory patients.

The central switchboard should be housed in a relatively sound proof room or booth. Additional equipment for it should include shelves for recordings and a telephone for which the usual bell signal is replaced by a light signal. An instantaneous record-cutter which permits the operator to record programs from the radio

or microphone will be found of great value, but the expense
involved may be too great for most hospitals of fewer than 500
beds.

It is most advisable that a full-time operator for the system
be employed. The operator should have a pleasant voice, but even
more important, a highly intelligible one. He will require some
basic training in the operation of the switchboard and its accessories
and this should be the obligation of the organization which installs
the equipment. The operator should be required to keep a written
record of everything that emanates from the studio. He should
be responsible for the routine care of the apparatus and know
enough about its parts to recognize defects early and to correct
some of the simpler ones. He must be prepared to live a lone life.
There is always a temptation to invite or permit guests in the
studio, and the resultant diversion or conversation might adversely
affect the broadcast.

If an instantaneous record cutter is available he should read
"How to Make Good Recordings" (Audak Co. of New York)
which is not only valuable for the recording of music but gives
some excellent advice concerning the use of the proper needle
for music reproduction and the use of the microphone.

PROGRAM

Music. The public address system should be operated on a
rigid schedule in imitation of a commercial radio studio. This is
necessary because the patients will come to expect certain features
at specified times of the day and fluctuations may result in disappointment and reduced morale. The program policy should be the
direct concern of the hospital superintendent and any service
chiefs who are interested. The hours of use will vary considerably
with the individual hospital from a few hours to a very full
program. Because of the great number of possible variations, some

general applications will be considered first and then a model program will be suggested.

The hour of awakening for patients may vary from about six to seven. At some time during that hour, a program of exhilarating music is indicated to start the day off right and perhaps get better cooperation between the patients and the nursing personnel in morning care. To this end, military or other marches are suggested as well as gay melodies, because as Seashore (73) has shown, "pronounced rhythm brings on a feeling of elation," and martial music is traditionally stirring. This program should last from fifteen to thirty minutes, and should be followed by silence for at least fifteen minutes before breakfast is served. It is unwise to begin eating while too stimulated.

During the breakfast, luncheon and supper periods, mealtime music should be broadcast for the entire duration of the dining period. The nature of mealtime music may be the same for all meals. This is discussed in Chapter VII.

The period between eight and ten in the morning is frequently reserved for routine dressings or medical rounds and a period of silence should be observed in the wards during the hours of maximum professional services. Obviously, music should not be broadcast at any time during the day when rounds are held. The operator should be supplied with a schedule of ward rounds and cut out those wards which are concerned.

The duration of rounds will vary from very brief periods on the surgical wards to prolonged ones on the medical wards. Soon after rounds the operator should broadcast to wards on which no regular activity is taking place. A half hour program of request music in the morning between ten and eleven is suggested. This should be followed by the pre-meal period of silence.

Where desired, luncheon music should be followed by restful or very soft music. If the blinds are drawn and silence among patients is maintained maximum benefit will result. Those patients who can fall asleep readily at this time will do so. Those who find it impossible to nap in the afternoon will be grateful for the diversion of music which will permit greater relaxation. It is more difficult for some people to rest in absolute quiet than with soft background music.

Another request program of music lasting one hour may be begun between two and three o'clock. It is advisable to mention specific names of patients who request music to stimulate patient interest in communal participation and listening. During the evening hours following supper, it is suggested that the most popular radio programs be transmitted over the system. These should be chosen on the bases of Hooper or Crossley ratings so that the greatest number of patients will be satisfied. When more than one channel is available, the second program selected should be of a different nature from the first.

Announcements. Announcements should be kept to a minimum. Routine announcements should be made at specified hours daily, such as after breakfast, before lunch, and after supper. Emergency calls should be limited to genuine emergencies or they will not be regarded as compelling, as they should be.

Newscasts are a much appreciated and desirable feature for patients who, until their admission to the hospital, may have read or listened to the news daily and will want to keep up with it. The newscast should be given in an unsensational manner and news which is too depressing or exciting should be deleted or reworded, for psychiatric patients.

Special Programs. There should be a weekly religious program sent out over the system for those in bed. The minister affiliated with the hospital should be able to fit the hospital into his Sunday morning schedule. If no minister is available, a regular radio program should be rebroadcast, but a Sunday service of local origin will be more personal, and therefore will be more appreciated. There are many suitable religious recordings available for incidental service music, particularly the series of albums pressed by Bibletone.

Holidays should be observed by the reproduction of appropriate music or radio rebroadcasts.

For the small hospital with limited personnel a two-channel system continuously tuned to the two most popular networks locally available, should be used.

CHAPTER TEN

EQUIPMENT AND LIBRARY

A hospital which wishes to use music as an adjunct to medical practice must be willing to offer the space required for its activities. The extent to which music will be needed will depend upon the nature of the illnesses treated and the average stay of the patients. For mental and tuberculosis hospitals, music is a "must." The chronic hospital usually has an assembly or recreation hall for musical performance. This hall will generally be adequate for band rehearsals, and may also be used at other hours of the day for instrumental practice. Where funds and space can be spared, additional rehearsal rooms should be built so that more patients will be able to participate. Space can be saved by building small cubicles sound-proofed with any of the sound absorbing fabricated wall boards such as *Celotex* or *Transite*. Cubicles should be built with much glazing so that the patient will not feel the smallness of the room. If there is only one music aide, there will be an advantage in centralizing all music activities, but if more help is available, music rehearsal rooms should be available in the different pavilions or wings of the hospital so that newly convalescent patients will not have to walk too far.

If the age range of the patient runs the full gamut, seating and instrumental provisions will have to include provisions for all. This means adjustable piano benches, music stands, etc. Chairs should be provided not only for musicians but spectators. Patients should be encouraged to attend band and other group rehearsals as a method of stimulating their interest in music and for the diversion which it will afford. Music stands for the bands should be dressed up to resemble those used by popular bands. These stands are colorful, collapsible, and hence transportable for any outside performances which the patient band may contract.

Instruments

Participation. The number and nature of instruments which a hospital should have will depend only upon budget limitations and the interest of the community. There is no limit except storage space to the number and variety of instruments which a hospital should accept as gifts. Ideally there should be at least one of each of the major instruments. Each instrument should have its own case, and it is wise to engrave the hospital name on each instrument to minimize loss. The initials of the hospital may be cut into an inconspicuous part of the instrument such as the inside of the brass bell or the under side of the wood body. All the instruments should be locked in cabinets when not in use.

In addition to regular band instruments, small instruments which can be played in bed should be acquired. These can be divided into those of normal construction such as the ukulele, mandolin, and autoharp and the toneless instruments which can be made by removing the resonating body. A toneless violin can be constructed from a donated violin in poor condition by mounting the tailpiece, bridge, and fingering element on a narrow strip of wood or plastic. A piece of rubber "kneeling" pad makes a good practice drum head.

For children toy instruments such as the Typatune, the toy-xylophone, trumpet, maracas, etc. should be available.

Listening. A room should be designated as a "Music Listening Room." For economy of use this may be a multi-purpose room. It may be a combination of the music aide's office and musical library used at selected hours of the day for both practice and listening. It should contain an instrument for playing recordings. The choice of record player should depend upon the sound produced by the instrument rather than its name. The record player for the listening room should have an automatic changer and wide tone control if possible. Because of the excellence of many musical broadcasts a combination radio-record player is most desirable.

Portable record players are also desirable for the bedside listening of those who request it. In hospitals not equipped with public address systems, the portable record player can act as an excellent substitute for it. If the player is mounted on a cart fitted with shelves for records and albums, it can be wheeled from one ward to another for daily musical periods. If the hospital has small-sized lantern slides with words to songs imprinted (such as those supplied Service groups during the war by the USO), a small slide projector should be added to the music cart to be used on the darkened ward for ward songs.

THE MUSIC LIBRARY

The hospital music library may vary from a few recordings to a composite collection of all forms of musical literature available. General hospitals which treat all diseases and age groups will require the most extensive and catholic varieties of all kinds of music. Specialty hospitals can operate on a library tailored to their individual needs. A hospital for the aged will not require too much of contemporary popular music. For purposes of inclusiveness, the ideal will be discussed in the hope that some hospitals will be able to afford it and that others will be able to select those items which become possible for them.

Recordings. The choice of recordings will be determined by the usual hospital population. In building up the record library the music aide should submit check lists to every patient in the hospital on any one day. The list should include ten specific titles in each of six categories: symphony, opera, operetta, folk-songs, old-time favorites, and the currently popular songs. These should be carefully tabulated and should be used to form the nucleus of the permanent collection. A space should be left for patients to write in other pieces than those named. Records should be purchased in the order of their numerically recorded popularity. A collection should begin with one record per hospital bed. This method of starting a library is very tedious but well worth the effort, because only by determining the musical tastes of patients can you give the majority the music they want. The musical tastes of the patients will not vary significantly after a complete turn-over in patient census, since most hospitals derive their patient population from the same geographic area, and the tabulation of musical desires arrived at in this manner will correspond satisfactorily with the tastes of the same age group in the community. If the budget will not permit an original collection of this size, it might be reduced to half of that recommended, but that is a minimum.

The collection should be built up at a rate of approximately one record for every ten new patient admissions. The choice of additional records should be on a request basis, but the proportion of the six categories as originally determined should remain relatively constant to keep the collection balanced.

Whenever there is a choice of two or more recordings of the same piece, the discs to choose are those which are played softly or sweetly so that they are adaptable for the additional purpose of mealtime or restful music.

In the library of recordings there should be included albums of records for special occasions and holidays. Patients look forward to hearing Irish songs on St. Patrick's Day and appropriate songs on other holidays. To accompany religious services the albums prepared by Bibletone are valuable. A glance through any standard record catalogue will readily permit the music aide to assemble a suitable collection.

The following is a list of records suggested for Easter Sunday and St. Patrick's Day.

Easter Recordings:

I Want a Bunny for Easter	Decca 18654-A
Easter Sunday With You	Decca 18591 B
Easter Parade	Decca 18425 B
Easter Sunday on the Prairie	Decca 18654 B
Chorale for Easter Cantata	Victor 15631 B
Requiem, by Gabriel Faure	Victor 18301, 2, 3, and 4

St. Patrick's Day:

Molly Brannigan	Columbia 35496
That's How I Spell Ireland	Columbia 35496
Come Back to Erin	Victor 27770 B
Mother Machree	Victor 27772 A
Eileen	Columbia 36585
A Little Bit of Heaven	Sonora 1069 B
You're Irish and You're Beautiful	Sonora 1068 A
Irish Lullaby	Decca 18621 A
Same Old Shellalagh	Columbia 354986
Macushla	Victor 27770 A
I'll Take You Home Again Kathleen	Sonora 1067 B
Little Town in Old County Down	Sonora 1070 B

All recordings should be kept in their albums or jackets. Because jackets have a way of getting lost or torn, there should be a stock of unused jackets on hand. Each jacket should be labelled according to its contents. In addition a cross-index catalogue file should be maintained by the music aide for all records in the hospital collection. Three cards should be filled out for each face of each record: one card for composer, one for title, and one for performer. This seems like a lot of work but is worth the effort because it is only in this manner that a program can be rapidly assembled from the record library. Any filing system will suffice, but if the collection is large, an elaborate system will be found worth the effort. Cards of three different colors may be used to separate classical, popular and miscellaneous. Tabs may be placed on those cards which list music for occasions. Tabs in one corner may refer to meal-time music and tabs in another holiday music, etc.

It is well to have the entire record collection in one room, and shelves for holding records should be built of very heavy lumber because recordings when closely packed are very heavy. It is best to add records to shelves with continuous acession numbers in each category and to rely on the file for alphabetic listing. If there are duplicates, they can form the nucleus for a second or lending library. Broken, cracked, or defective discs should be placed in a separate section of the shelves for replacement when budget permits and popularity demands.

Instantaneous Recordings. A few hospitals will have the good fortune to acquire a record-cutter for hospital recording of radio music. When this is possible, the record collection can be augmented most satisfactorily. The music aide should study all radio programs to determine the hours during which the best performances of desired music are played. By listening to several carefully selected programs each week he will soon discover which programs use music employed in a manner most desirable for hospital reproduction. The orchestrations of Kostelanetz and Lombardo are especially suitable for easy listening in the field of popular music. The broadcasts of the Metropolitan Opera Association include passages not commercially recorded or at least not recorded with the most popular singers. There are many other radio features which are worth recording for the hospital record library.

It is relatively easy to operate a record-cutter, but there are many minor details which must be known for maximum efficiency. An excellent book for beginners is that published by the Audak Company of New York, *How to Make Good Recordings.*

Sheet Music. A library of sheet music will once more depend upon the local needs. It may include orchestral, instrumental, vocal, and band music. In the hospital for the chronically ill, a large number of varieties will be needed. Inasmuch as the simplest group performance will be vocal, music for group singing should head the list. The music should include old-time favorites, hymns, spirituals and any other items which the aide can determine from the intellectual and musical qualifications and desires of the patients. This type of music can be purchased individually and increased according to the interest shown.

If there is a patient band, the musical scores should include a few marches which may be used at the beginning and end of its concerts. The perennial favorites most desirable for community singing should constitute a major portion of the orchestral literature. The readily available medleys of Victor Herbert melodies and similar stand-bys can complete the initial group.

Sheet music should be catalogued and filed in cabinets. A simple system of shelving consists of grouping music according to use: one shelf for group playing, one for solo and beginners instrumental books, and another for vocal selections. The numbers most commonly and currently used by the band can be placed in folders according to the accepted usage among bands, and if there are daily rehearsals they can remain on the band stands at all times.

The library should also contain books, printed forms, or mimeographed collections of songs for distribution to patients during community singing.

Books About Music. The average hospital library will have relatively few books about musical appreciation or history. This will depend first on the budget and second on the demand. The addition of a music aide to a hospital staff will usually increase the demand. The music aide should be consulted concerning the books he thinks will appeal to patients. Books on music should also be available to help the music aide in preparing commentaries on the music he plays for the patients.

The following are some books suggested for inclusion in the hospital patient library:

> Copland, Aaron—*What to Listen for in Music,* 1939.
> Goss, Madeline—*Unfinished Symphony,* 1941.
> Elson, Arthur—*Music Club Programs From All Nations.*
> Erskine, John—*What Is Music,* 1944.
> Ewen, David—*Tales From The Vienna Woods,* 1944.
> Ewen, David—*Gershwin's Life,* 1944.
> Ewen, David—*Men of Popular Music,* 1944.
> Gronowicz, Antoni—*Chopin,* 1943.
> O'Connell, Charles—*Victor Book of Opera,* 1936.
> Taylor, Deems—*Of Men and Music,* 1945.
> Taylor, Deems—*The Well Tempered Listener,* 1944.
> Siegmeister, Elie—*Music Lover's Handbook,* 1943.
> Spaeth, Sigmund—*At Home With Music,* 1945.

For young patients there are the new series of colorfully illustrated lives of composers from Bach to Gershwin by Waldo Mayo, as well as a great number of old and good titles.

CHAPTER ELEVEN

DIRECTION

The introduction of music into the hospital will depend not so much upon its proven value as an aid to medical practice as upon the interest of someone on the staff who loves music or recognizes its importance in the mental hygiene of the patients. There are many reasons for the absence of music in some hospitals which may seem difficult for the musician to comprehend. The acceptance of a music program in a hospital calls for increased budget and space. These are two items which constantly beset the hospital director and they are sometimes matters of improbable solution. For the chronic type of hospital the problem must be solved. Other drawbacks are found in the contemplated interference of medical and nursing procedures. Hospitals are traditionally havens of quiet and the uninformed hospital director or his staff may envisage a conversion to a three-ringed circus of sound. The progress of music in hospitals will depend largely upon the ingenuity and intelligence of existing organizations and the examples they can set for prospective hospitals.

The musical program of a hospital need not necessarily be conducted by a musician, but a trained person is most desirable. There are people with an intense love for music and so comprehensive a grasp of its many fields that they might be capable of conducting a hospital program although unable to play an instrument. At some institutions music has been guided by volunteers with great satisfaction to staff and patients, but this is an age of specialization and a paid, trained musician will usually be worth the salary in efficiency, dependability, and control.

DIRECTOR

Music for patients differs from music for the well. The average musician is not qualified to decide which patients should or should not have music. There are too many well meaning musicians who have had one or two personal experiences or heard of others in which the efforts of the musician were rewarded by apparent miracles of mental reaction. Musicians are not capable of evaluating such changes nor do they bother to recount what the condition of the patient was an hour or a day after this personal exposure. Musicians must have medical direction. The medical director of music does not have to be a trained musician but he should be acquainted in a general way with most musical forms which appeal to a majority of patients. His most important qualification will be the ability to rise above personal prejudices of musical taste. He must recognize that musical tastes can be as diverse as individual appetites for different foods, and feel free to order music as he would food for patients. It will be his duty to prescribe quantity, quality, duration, and intervals of music; to contraindicate music for the irritable, certain post-operative patients, the acutely ill, and any others for whom he thinks music is wrong. It will be necessary for him to protect the patients from the possible musical whims, hobbies, convictions or over-enthusiasm of the musical aide.

The director should be selected from volunteers on the staff. For the physician director of music to be chosen in any other way is to hamper the musical program. He must be a physician who has the time or can make the time to carry out his part adequately. At the outset the director should have daily conferences with the senior musical aide in which he should not only outline the pro-

cedures desired but should observe the musician at work with
patients.

Music Aide

There is considerable disagreement concerning the title most
desirable for the person conducting music in the hospital. The
term "musical therapist" implies a training not only in music but
in treatment. The occupational therapist has had a training not
only in crafts, but in basic medical subjects, psychology, and some
clinical subjects. Until musicians can take similar courses at
accredited schools a different title seems wiser. At some hospitals
the workers are called recreational aides, but such people also
conduct other recreational activities. It seems picayune to argue
over terminology, but the hospital music worker must be called
something and it is hard to conceive that anyone would find fault
with the appelation "music aide" for those people who bring music
to the patient.

A music aide may be of either sex and of any age. The choice
will depend not only upon what is available locally but on such
considerations as the personalities involved and personal recommendations. If intelligence is not exercised, the program will fail
because the senior music aide is the keystone of the entire structure.
For a children's hospital, a woman who has raised children would
seem most suitable. The aide for children should be able to sing
and play the piano. She should also be able to play musical games
with children.

For a hospital of young adults, such as the average hospital
for the tuberculous, a young woman between thirty and forty will
have the energy, drive and spirit to match the requirements and
contemporary tastes of the patients under her care. The aide for
this type of work should also be able to lead group and mass

singing and be able to play an instrument. Ability to play a second instrument, or to teach it is a valuable asset.

For the mental hospital an aide should be mature, patient, well informed and have the urge, but not the preformed opinions, for handling the mental patient. For the hospital treating the aged or other chronic patients, an older man or woman is desirable.

It is preferable for any aide to have had some formal musical instruction. Most desirable is a graduate of a musical conservatory or of a college which offers a major in music. The music aide should play at least one instrument, and preferably the piano. If the hospital budget permits additional music aides each successive one should know another instrument. The aide should be able to play music at sight and sing with an acceptable voice. The chief qualification should be the absence of "artistic temperament." Patients are admitted to a hospital for medical care, not musical knowledge. The aide should not consider them as music students. Music should be given to them with patience and without undue emotion. If music evokes a marked mental response it may be beneficial, but it should be the music and not the musician which elicits such reactions. Previous experience in teaching music is a valuable asset to the music aide.

The duties of the music aide will vary with the number and type of patients. In hospitals with a large number of ambulatory patients emphasis will be placed on group activities; in hospitals where children predominate music will be used largely as diversion, in games, dancing and other bodily activities called "rhythms" which is a development of Eurythmics.

Under the supervision of the medical director, the music aide should outline a definite schedule of musical activities and adhere to it. This will require much preparation and the best hours for preparatory work will be those during which patients are resting, sleeping, or receiving active medical and nursing care. The preparation will include maintenance and cataloguing of instruments and the medical library; tabulation of patient requests for instruction, books and recordings; programing for concerts, ward songs and the public address system; correspondence with musicians and musical groups in the community; ordering of equipment and music; and scheduling.

The schedule should be patterned to fit into the hospital routine. The first hour of the day should be reserved for preparatory activities. Individual instruction in music may be given from nine until ten. At ten the music cart may be taken to the wards until mealtime. Following the meal hour, the aide can prepare for the afternoon ward visits. Recreation Hall activities or the listening room may be scheduled for the period of two to three. Three to four-thirty may be used for ward entertainment, either with the music cart or with portable instruments. On one or two nights a weeks, an hour or more may be set aside for the hospital concert or a music appreciation hour.

TRAINING

At present no accredited school of music or medicine offers a complete course of instruction leading to a degree in music in medical practice, or a major in that subject. It is believed that eventually the demand may bring about the establishment of such a course in a musical college, where it belongs. It will be necessary for the school of music to secure liaison with a medical college or school of occupational therapy and this will limit instruction to those cities where grade A institutions of both kinds are to be found. There are at least ten cities scattered throughout the United States in which this happy combination may be found, but there is hardly need for more than six.

Applicants should be interviewed by a representative of both the medical and music schools. A projected curriculum is suggested as follows:

First Year

Piano	8 Credits
Solfège	5 Credits
Counterpoint	2 Credits
Harmony	2 Credits
English	6 Credits
History of Medicine	1 Credit

Second Year

Piano	4 Credits
Solfège	2 Credits
Harmony	2 Credits
Counterpoint	2 Credits
History of Music	4 Credits
Nursing anatomy	6 Credits

Third Year

Violin	4 Credits
Harmony	4 Credits
Musical Form	4 Credits
Physics	6 Credits
Physiology	2 Credits
Kinesiology	2 Credits
Psychology	4 Credits
Conducting	2 Credits
Piano Sight Playing	4 Credits
Ensemble	2 Credits

Fourth Year

Violin	4 Credits
Choral Class	0 Credits
Conducting	2 Credits
Contemporary Music	4 Credits
Occupational Therapy	4 Credits
Music in Medicine	6 Credits
Abnormal Psychology	6 Credits
Orchestra Reading	2 Credits

A brief explanation of courses not normally found at music schools and which should be given at medical or professional schools follows.

Anatomy for Nurses. This should consist of a brief survey of the anatomy of the human body with especial reference to the muscles, nerves, brain, and a casual introduction to the internal organs.

History of Medicine. This would be an orientation course on the development of medicine and hospitals.

Physiology. Especial attention should be drawn to the physiology of the nervous system and the muscles.

Psychology. Normal psychology, including laboratory experimentation in the psychology of music, would be the basis of this course.

Kinesiology. The standard course as taught in schools of physical and occupational therapy, and physical education, would be sufficient.

Occupational Therapy. An introduction into craft analysis and psychiatric occupational therapy is necessary.

Abnormal Psychology. An introduction to psychiatry is sufficient.

Music in Medicine. A course of lectures, including the subjects discussed in this volume, should be offered.

In the summer between the third and fourth years, the student should be affiliated with a hospital with a music program to work under the hospital staff.

These are suggestions only, and each school in consultation with an approved medical college will want to work out its own schedule. It is hoped that the above outline will be of definite assistance.

BIBLIOGRAPHY

(1) Albrecht, W.,   De effect. mus., Sect. 314, *in Roger, J. L.*

(2) Altschuler, I.,   *Occ. Ther. Rehab.,* 1941, 20:75.

(3) Altschuler, I.,   *Proc. Mus. Teach. Nat. Assoc.,* 1944, p. 154.

(4) Altschuler, I., and
Shebesta, B.,   *Journ. Nerv. Ment. Dis.* 1941, 94:179.

(5) Ayers, I.,   *Am. Phys. Ed Rev.,* 1912, 16:321.

(6) Barker, L.,   *Psychotherapy,* New York, 1940.

(7) Bauer, M., and
Peyser, E.,   *Music Through the Ages,* New York, 1932.

(8) Beaunis, B.,   "L'Emotion Musicale", *Rev. Phil.,* 1918, 86:353.

(9) Beckett, W.,   *Music in War Plants,* Washington, 1943

(10) Bissell, A. D.,   The Role of Expectation in Music, New Haven, 1921

(11) Boerhaave, H.,   Impetum Faciens, *in Roger, J. L.*

(12) Bowers, C. G.,   *The Young Jefferson,* New York, 1945.

(13) Brocklesby, R.,   *Reflections on Antient and Modern Musick,* London, 1749.

(14) Bücher, K.,   Arbeit und Rhythmus, *in Diserens, C. M.*

(15) Burney, Charles.,   *A General History of Music,* Ed., by Mercer, F., New York, 1937.

(16) Celsus, A. C.,   *Of Medicine,* Trans, by J. Grieve, London, 1838.

(17) Champlain,   Voyages de l'Amerique, *in Roger, J. L.*

(18) Chomet, H.,   *Influence of Music in Health and Life,* New York, 1875.

(19) Combarieu, J.,   *La Musique, Ses Lois, Son Evolution,* Paris, 1907

(20) Damon, K. F.,   Program Notes for the Listener to music, New York, 1933

(21) Densmore, Frances.,   *American Indians and Their Music,* New York, 1926

(22) Densmore, Frances   *Teton Sioux Music,* Bull. 61, Smithsonian Inst., Washington, D. C.

(23) Desault, P.,   Method pour preserver de la rage, *in Roger, J. L.*

(24) Diserens, C. M.,   *Influence of Music on Behaviour,* Princeton, 1926.

(25) D'Olivet, F.,   *La Musique,* Paris, 1896

(26) Dunlap, K.,   Rhythm and the Specious Present, *J. Phil. Psychol. and Sci. Method,* 1911, 8:348.

(27) Dupre, E., and Nathan, M.,   *Le Language Musical,* Paris, 1911.

(28) Eastcott, Richard   Sketches of the Origin, Progress and Effects of Music, Bath, 1748.

(29) Eby, J.,   *Occ. Ther. Rehab.,* 1943, 22:31.

(30) Galton, F.,   Inquiries Into Human Faculty and Its Development, London, 1883.

(31) Gaston, E.,   *Music Educ.* 1945, 31:24

(32) Gatewood, E.,   *Am. J. Surg.,* 1921, 35:47.

(33) Gatewood, E.,   *J. App. Psychol.,* 1921, 5:350.

(34) Gehring, A.,   *Basis of Musical Pleasure,* New York, 1910.

(35) Gilman, B.,   Report on an Experimental Test of Musical Expressiveness, *Amer. J. Psychol.,* 1892, 4:42.

(36) Gray, C.,   Contingencies, *The Music Review,* Nov. 1944.

(37) Gruner, O. C.,   *The Canon of Medicine of Avicenna,* London, 1930

(38) Gundlach, R.,   An Analysis of Some Musical Factors Determining the Mood Characteristics of Music, *Psychol. Bull.,* 1934, 31:592.

(39) Gundlach, R.,   A Quantitave Analysis of Indian Music, *Am. J. Psychol.,* 1932, 44:133.

(40) Gurney, E.,   *The Power of Sound,* London, 1880.

(41) Hanson, H.,   Some Objective Studies of Rhythm in Music. *Am. J. Psychiatry,* Nov. 1944, 101:364

(42) Hanson, H.,   Musician's Point of View Toward Emotional
                                 Expression, *Am. J. Psychiatry,* Nov. 1942,
                                 99:317

(43) Harrington, A.,   Ment. Hyg., 1939, 23:601.
(44) Hauptman, M.,   Die Natur de Harmonik, *in Helmholtz,*
                                 H. L. F.

(45) Heinlein, C. P.,   The Affective Characters of the Major and
                                 Minor Mode in Music, *J. Comp. Psychol.,*
                                 1928, 8:101.

(46) Helmholtz, H. L. F.,   *The Sensations of Tone,* London, 1875.
(47) Hevner, K.,   The Affective Character of the Major and
                                 Minor Modes in Music, *Am. J. Psychol.,*
                                 1935, 47:**103.**

(48) Hevner, K.,   The Affective Value of Pitch and Tempo in
                                 Music, *Amer. J. Psychol.,* 1937, 49:621.

(49) Hulbert, H.,   *Eurthym.,* London, 1921.
(50) Jacobson, E.,   Electrophsiology of Mental Activities, *Am. J.*
                                 Psychol., 1932, 44:677.

(51) Johnson, M.,   *Nat. Ed. Ass. Journ.,* 1905, 45:940.
(52) Kawarski, T., and
     Odbert, H.,   Color Music, *Psychol. Monographs,* 1938,
                                 no. 50.

(53) Kirschner, M.,   Musik und Operation, *Der Chirurg,* 1936,
                                 11:429.

(54) Kraines, S.,   *The Therapy of Neuroses and Psychoses,*
                                 Phila., 1943

(55) Lee, V.,   *Music and Its Lovers,* London, 1930.
(56) Levine, M.,   *Psychotherapy in Medical Practice,* New
                                 York, 1942

(57) Ligeros, K. A.,   *How Ancient Healing Governs Modern*
                                 Therapeutics, New York, 1937.

(58) Meibomius, M.,   *Antiquae Musicae Auctores,* Lib. IX,
                                 Amstelodami, 1652.

(59) Mueller, J., and
     Hevner, K.,   Trends in Musical Taste, *Indiana U. Public.,*
                                 1942, no. 8.

(60) Mursell, J. L.,   *Psychology of Music*, New York, 1937.
(61) Nollet, J. A.,   *Recherches sur les Causes Particulieres des Phenomènes Electriques*, Paris, 1749, p 33.
(62) Noyes, A. P.,   *Modern Clinical Psychiatry*, Phila., 1944.
(63)   *The Old Testament*, I Samuel, Chap. 16, verse 23.
(64) Ortmann, Otto   *The Physiologic Mechanics of Piano Technique*, London, 1929.
(65) Pearson, Hesketh,   *G. B. S.*, New York, 1942
(66) Pierce, A.,   *Med. Bull. Vet. Adm.*, 1934, 21:142.
(67) Porta, J. B.,   Magia natural., *in Roger, J. L.*
(68) Rameau, J. P.,   *Traité de l'harmonie*, Paris, 1722.
(69) Reade, W.,   African Sketch Book, *in Diserens.*
(70) Roger, J. L.,   *Effects de le Musique*, Paris, 1803.
(71) Schoen, M.,   *The Effects of Music*, London, 1927.
(72) Schoen, M.,   *The Psychology of Music*, New York, 1940.
(73) Seashore, K.,   *Psychology of Music*, New York, 1938.
(74) Tarchanoff, I.,   *Arch. Italien, de Biol.*, 26:313.
(75) Thorndike, L.,   *A History of Magic*, vol. 2, New York, 1923
(76) Valentine, C.,   The Aesthetic Appreciation of Musical Intervals Among Children and Adults, *Brit. J. Psychol.*, 1944, 6:190.
(77) Vernon, P. E.,   Auditory Perception, *Brit. J. Psychol.*, 1934, 25:123.
(78) Vescelius, E.,   *Music and Health*, New York, 1927.
(79) Wallaschek, R.,   *Primitive Music*, London, 1893.
(80) Wedge, G.,   *Keyboard Harmony*, New York, 1924.
(81) Willis, T.,   *Cerebri Anatome Nervorumque*, cap. XVII, Amstelodami, 1664.

INDEX